RADIO NAVIGATION FOR PILOTS

(*Frontispiece.*)

RADIO NAVIGATION FOR PILOTS

BY

COLIN H. McINTOSH

*Assistant Superintendent of Flying
School Operations, Military Division,
American Airlines, Inc.*

FIRST EDITION
FOURTH IMPRESSION

McGRAW-HILL BOOK COMPANY, INC.

NEW YORK AND LONDON

1943

RADIO NAVIGATION FOR PILOTS

PREFACE

The purpose of this book is to provide the average pilot with a brief and nontechnical presentation of radio-navigation techniques. With this in mind, every effort has been made to maintain the discussion of the subject matter on a practical plane. In keeping with this objective, then, the popular-science method of presentation designed primarily to inform the nonflying layman has been deliberately avoided. At the same time, all academic theory and technical data of interest only to the technician have been omitted. Instead, a middle ground between these extremes has been followed. From the great mass of material on the subject of radio navigation, only the basic information and essential techniques that a pilot needs have been selected. This selected material has then been treated in sufficient detail to provide a pilot with a good working knowledge of the subject.

It should be noted that the contents of this book have likewise been limited to a discussion of radio navigation. No attempt has been made to introduce instrument flight techniques. Although instrument flying is often considered synonymous with radio navigation, owing to the fact that radio has become the primary means of navigating when "on instruments," actually two distinct techniques are involved. Strictly interpreted, instrument flying is the art of *controlling* an airplane by instrument indications; radio navigation is concerned primarily with directing the airplane to some desired destination. It should be apparent that any flight may be made entirely on instruments and yet involve no radio navigation. Likewise, radio navigation may be practiced whether on instruments or flying ground contact. As a matter of fact, most airline procedures are based upon radio navigation in either case.

The above distinction between instrument flying and radio navigation is brought out to emphasize the difference in approach that can be followed to achieve a safe and precise technique in either art. Summarized, it may be said that the ability to fly on instruments can best be developed by constant practice in an airplane—preferably the same type of airplane—so as to achieve the high degree of visual and physical coordination needed for a precise and safe technique in maneuvering and control. Radio navigation, on the other hand, may be considered largely a mental problem. The ability to visualize the problem at hand by interpreting radio signals into a mental diagram is of utmost importance. The development of such skill is primarily a matter of mental training, much of which can be done solely on paper or, better still, by well-directed instruction and practice in the Link Trainer.

Various portions of this book have appeared in slightly different form as separate articles in *The Sportsman Pilot* and *Aviation*. The author is indebted to the editorial staffs of these magazines for much help and constructive criticism during the composition of the original articles. He would also like to thank Mr. Walter Braznell and Mr. Buell Patterson, both of American Airlines, for their cooperation and assistance. Likewise, many of the ideas and techniques set forth have crystallized in present form as the result of innumerable hours of instruction and discussion with flight personnel of American Airlines at Chicago.

C. H. McINTOSH.

CHICAGO,
November, 1942.

CONTENTS

RADIO NAVIGATION FOR PILOTS

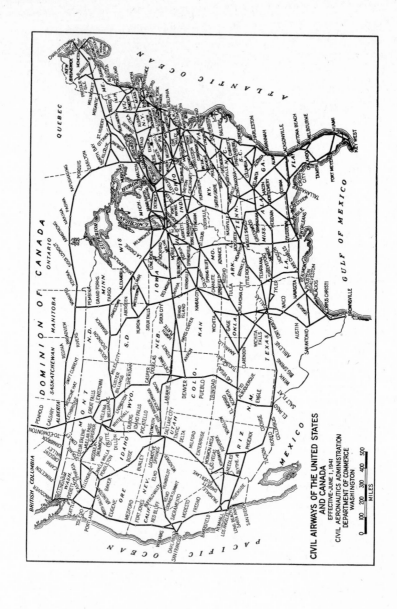

CIVIL AIRWAYS OF THE UNITED STATES
AND CANADA
EFFECTIVE-JUNE 1, 1941
CIVIL AERONAUTICS ADMINISTRATION
DEPARTMENT OF COMMERCE
WASHINGTON

0   100   200   300   400   500
MILES

CHAPTER I

RADIO-NAVIGATION SYSTEMS

Radio navigation as applied to aircraft may be defined in simple terms as the art of conducting the flight of an aircraft from one position to another over the earth's surface by the use of radio signals for directional guidance.

Since it is directional aid (used in the sense of providing directional indication in a plane parallel to the earth's surface) that becomes the prerequisite for navigation, the presumption is either that the radio energy radiated from the transmitter is directional in character or that the receivers picking it up do so in a manner to provide the required directional sense. Both of these basic principles are used.

DIRECTIONAL-TRANSMITTER SYSTEM

Within the continental United States, of course, as well as Canada and Alaska, the primary method of providing navigational aid for aircraft is by means of the familiar network of radio range stations. This best exemplifies the practical adaptation of the directional transmitter.

These radio ranges as now used in the United States are specially designed ground transmitters for aeronautical use only. A and N signals in international code are transmitted in such fashion from directional antennas as to form four so-called "radio beams" radiating from the transmitter site. By proper control of the radiated energy, these beams may be projected in any desired direction. Usually they are directed along the center line of specified civil airways; thus

3

pilots are provided with a radio defined pathway for navigational guidance. In addition to the navigational aid these range stations provide, they are used for voice communication between ground control centers and airplanes in flight, transmission of weather reports, traffic instructions to pilots, and other information.

Unquestionably, the radio range network as maintained in the United States represents the finest and most complete system of radio aids for aircraft navigation existing in the world. Several distinct advantages of this system over alternative means of radio navigation should be pointed out.

1. It is a federally operated system of navigation aids available to any aircraft equipped with a simple receiver capable of operating on the proper frequencies.

2. Stations are in continuous operation.

3. An unlimited number of aircraft may make use of any one station simultaneously just as millions of people may listen to the same broadcast station. In practice, of course, air space and traffic limitations do provide a restricting factor.

4. Since the radio beams are fixed in direction and are continuously available, their locations with respect to the earth may be added to aeronautical charts.

5. The permanent character of the beams provides an ideal means of delineating the airways and expediting the control of airway traffic.

6. Properly placed in relation to airports, range stations provide an excellent means of navigational guidance for instrument approaches during adverse weather.

7. The voice broadcasting facilities incorporated with each range station provide an unexcelled communications network for the transmission of information, weather reports, and instructions to pilots in flight.

Nevertheless, and in common with other navigational methods, the radio range system *by itself* does not provide the ideal means of navigational aid for aircraft. Detracting from the several advantages mentioned are several distinct limitations. Many of these, unfortunately, are more apparent to the individual pilot in flight than they are in theory.

Douglas DC-3 cockpit, fully equipped for radio navigation. (*Courtesy of American Airlines, Inc.*)

1. From a purely navigational standpoint, the radio range system is inflexible. Each range provides only four fixed beam courses to or from the station.

2. The direction of the beams is not governed by the choice of the pilot but is determined and fixed to mark specified airways.

3. Direct-line navigation for any great distance is usually impractical, as beam alignments of successive ranges seldom provide a straight airway. For example, to fly the radio range courses from Chicago to Detroit City Airport, a distance of 257 miles, necessitates six different courses.

4. Off-airway flying is made difficult because beams are seldom advantageously placed.

5. Aural reception of range signals makes it difficult to fly the beams with precision. In addition, the frequencies now used are extremely susceptible to static interference which frequently renders the signals unintelligible.

6. Numerous atmospheric and terrain factors interfere with the directional stability of the beams, often to the extent of making them unreliable and dangerous to follow.

7. Equipped with conventional receiving apparatus only, it is easy for a pilot to become confused regarding position on a range. Orientation is often difficult and time consuming.

Although it may appear that the foregoing analysis of the advantages and disadvantages of the radio range system is unwarranted at this point, it has been included to provide a basis for comparison with direction-finding systems to be subsequently discussed.

DIRECTION-FINDING RECEIVER SYSTEMS

The alternate principle to the radio range system for radio navigation is the use of receiving apparatus of directional sensing character. Such apparatus is commonly termed one of the following: a radio direction finder, a D/F loop receiver, or a radio compass. As will be explained later, however, a technical difference exists between a radio direction finder and a radio compass.

In general terms, such receiving equipment makes it possible to establish a directional bearing on any type of radio transmitter within the sensitivity and frequency ranges of the receiver. Practical adaptation of this principle follows two fundamental systems.

Ground Direction Finders.—With this system, the direction finders are specially designed ground receiver and antenna arrangements whereby a directional indication or radio bearing may be established on an aircraft transmitter. Where possible, such a system envisions a network of stations strategically situated throughout the area to be guarded, so that two or more stations can take simultaneous bearings on the same aircraft. By plotting the point of intersection of two or more of these lines of bearing, the airplane's position can be established. This may be done on the ground and the resultant solution of position radioed to the pilot, or the bearings can be given to the pilot for his own plot of position. Both techniques are used.

Marine navigators have long used such a system of direction finding provided by a Federal network of stations located along the seaboard of the United States and on the Great Lakes. In the aircraft field, Pan American Airways has employed a similar system of radio aid for transoceanic navigation. Because of the great distances over which it is desired to take bearings in this service, however, it has been necessary to abandon the more reliable low frequencies in favor of the moderately high frequencies (aircraft communication bands). From experience in the use of the same, the author is convinced that high-frequency direction-finding technique is not yet sufficiently developed to be considered reliable and accurate.

Aircraft Direction Finders.—The reverse method of carrying the direction finder in the airplane itself has found much more widespread use than the method just described.

With this arrangement, the pilot or navigator is able to

take his own bearings at will on any ground transmitters within the capabilities of the receiver and to work out his own navigational problems with a minimum of dependence upon ground personnel. In all respects, the system is more flexible in practice than ground direction finding. The numerous different methods in which aircraft D/F equipment may be employed will be more apparent with later discussion. For these reasons, as well as the economy with which aircraft can be equipped with direction finders, this system has long been a primary means of radio navigation in portions of the world where a radio range or ground direction-finding network does not exist.

Even though radio navigation in the United States is still governed fundamentally by the radio ranges, the use of aircraft direction-finding equipment is becoming almost universal. It has, in fact, been compulsory for scheduled airline operations since 1937. Likewise, practically all military aircraft in recent years have been so equipped.

COMPLEMENTARY SYSTEMS

After a thorough study has been made of the material to follow on both radio range navigation and direction finding, it should become apparent that neither means by itself furnishes the complete solution to air navigation by radio. Each method has several disadvantages. Fortunately, the disadvantages of one system are counteracted by the advantages of the other. Thus, to be completely equipped to navigate safely by radio, a pilot should be thoroughly conversant with both methods.

CHAPTER II

THE RADIO RANGE SYSTEM

Although the fundamental ideas of radio range navigation are very simple, the *actual execution* of many navigational problems on the radio ranges is very likely to be much less simple than their theoretical conception. It is easy to conceive of getting on a beam and following it to the radio station, or perhaps repeating this several times in order to fly an airway cross country. To navigate with precision and safety on the radio ranges actually takes much more than an understanding of abstract navigational principles. More important prerequisites are an intelligent appreciation of radio range operation and characteristics plus good instruction and constant practice flying range signals. In fact, the essence of radio range navigation is the *practical execution*. Thus, radio range flying becomes the more descriptive term.

ANTENNAS

In the previous chapter, the terms "directional transmitter" and "directional receiver" were used as generalizations to differentiate between the basic ideas underlying the range system and the direction-finder system of radio navigation. Strictly speaking, the application of the term "directional" to either a radio transmitter or a receiver is incorrect.

It is neither the transmitter nor the receiver which furnishes the directional character to radio energy. This is purely a function of the antenna from which the energy is either transmitted or on which it is received.

9

Conventional antennas for either transmission or reception can be considered, as a whole, nondirectional. That is, they either transmit or receive radio energy with approximately the same efficiency in all directions; or, if they do possess any directional character, it is in such small degree as to render them extremely inefficient in a directional sense. Among these nondirectional antennas are the single vertical mast so common to commercial broadcast stations, the multi-wire flat top used on ships and to a lesser degree by shore stations, and the usual single straight wire home receiving antenna.

Theory of Loop Antenna.—It has long been known, however, that a closed loop or coil of wire makes a radio antenna that is highly directional for either transmission or reception. This is not surprising since the action of such a coil used as a radio antenna conforms in all respects to the same electromagnetic principles that govern the use of any closed coil in electrical circuits. The electrical theory underlying the directional action of the loop may be summarized in the following manner.

Whenever a closed coil of wire is charged with an alternating electrical current, a similar alternating electromagnetic field of force is produced about the coil. Moreover, the field of force produced about the coil is not of equal intensity in all directions. It is greatest in a plane parallel to the coil and decreases theoretically to zero in a plane at right angles to the coil. Refer to Fig. 1. If this alternating current is of radio frequency, the coil is acting as a directional antenna for the transmission of a radio field of force. The above distinctive properties of a loop make possible the directional radio transmitting station.

The action of a closed loop used as a receiving antenna is almost diametrically opposite. When an alternating electromagnetic field of force is imposed upon a coil of wire, an alternating electrical current is produced in the coil. Radio energy, of course, is nothing more than an alternating electromagnetic field of radio frequency. As this is imposed upon the coil of the loop used as a receiving antenna, radio-frequency current is induced in the loop. The action of a loop for reception is also directional. The voltage of the current induced in the coil is directly dependent upon the angle with which the plane of the loop meets the incoming radio wave. When the plane of the loop is parallel to the direction of wave travel (pointed at the transmitter), the induced voltage in the

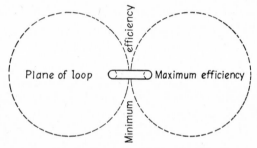

FIG. 1.—Loop-signal field strength.

coil is at a maximum. Conversely, with the plane of the loop perpendicular to the direction of wave travel (at right angles to the transmitter), the induced voltage is zero. Again refer to Fig. 1.

THE RADIO RANGE

Until approximately 1938, most radio range stations used an antenna in the form of two closed vertical loops placed at right angles to one another. The Adcock type of radio range station, however, accomplishes the same directional trans-mission as the loops by means of two pairs of vertical towers at right angles to one another. In addition, the vertical tow-ers form a more rigid antenna construction and keep the directional quality of the signals more stable.

At present, the majority of radio ranges are of this Adcock type further modified to provide simultaneous transmission of voice and range signals. This eliminates the annoyance—characteristic of the former loop-type stations—of shutting off the range signals whenever voice broadcasts are made. With the present type of station, a pilot may receive either range signals or voice, separately or both together, through a simple filtering switch on his receiver. All service-type range

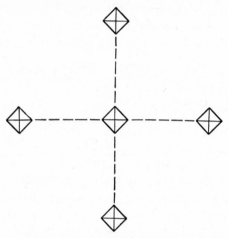

Fig. 2.—Radio-range-tower grouping. Broken lines indicate how towers are paired to form two antennas.

stations at present operate on a long wave, or low-frequency band, between 200 and 400 kilocycles.

In physical appearance, a radio range station consists of five vertical steel towers approximately 125 ft. high. Four of these are placed so as to form a square with each tower as a corner. The fifth tower is placed at the center. The purpose of these towers is to form the antennas of the station; the four towers forming the square being used for the directional radio signals, and the fifth tower in the center being used solely for the transmission of voice broadcasts. This center tower is nondirectional, *i.e.*, the voice broadcasts can be heard equally well in all directions.

The four vertical towers forming the square proper provide two transmitting antennas at right angles to one another for sending out the directional signals of the range station. This is accomplished by pairing each two towers at diagonally opposing corners of the square (refer to Fig. 2).

To each of these two antennas, a coded signal is fed by a single radio transmitter. This is done through a mechanical cam and keying system which sends out the signal N (— ·) on one antenna while the signal A (· —) is being sent on the other. In addition, the cams and keys are so timed that the

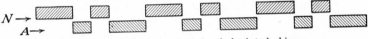

Fig. 3.—Timing of *A* and *N* signals for interlocking.

signal sequence is interlocking; *i.e.*, as the dash dot of the N is being sent on one antenna, the dot dash of the A is being timed on the second antenna in such a manner that the dot of the A fills the interval between the dash and dot of the N, and the dash of the A fills the interval after the dot of the N, etc. (refer to Fig. 3).

It will be apparent that, if the signals from both the A and the N antennas are heard with *equal strength*, neither an A nor an N will be heard; but owing to the interlocking of dots and dashes, only a steady dash will be heard. This is termed the "on-course" signal which forms the radio beam.

Thus, referring to Fig. 4, it will be seen that, if an N signal is sent from one pair of towers and an A signal from the other pair, the two signals will be sent out in the pattern of two figure 8's at right angles to one another. Each signal will be heard only within the boundaries of its own particular field. In this figure, three lines of force are drawn radiating from each antenna. It will be apparent upon inspection that these lines of force radiate strongest in line with the antennas and grow progressively weaker toward a plane at 90° to the loop. In four sectors, the lines of force from opposing antennas overlap one another. Within these zones, the A signal and the N signal are both present, though in *unequal* strength. On one narrow line, however, in each of these zones, where opposing lines of force intersect, the strength of the A and the N signals will be equal.

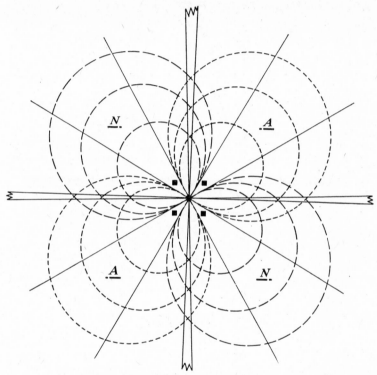

Fig. 4.—Theoretical radiation field for 90° range.

Translating the above discussion from technical terms, we may arrive at the following conclusions. In those zones, wherein only one signal is present, either an A or an N, a pilot will receive only an A or an N. Thus, there will be two pure A signal zones and two pure N signal zones, commonly termed "quadrants." If, however, a pilot is in one of the four zones in which both A and N signals are present, he will receive a combined signal formed by their interlocking. The stronger signal will predominate and may be distinguished, whereas the weaker signal blends in to form a steady dash in the background. These are termed "bi-signal zones."

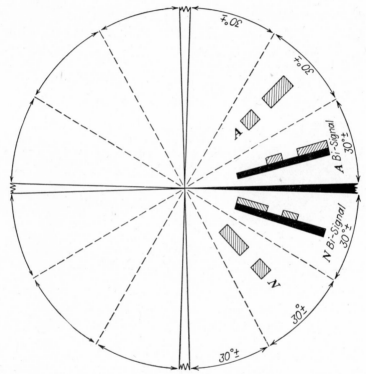

Fig. 5.—Theoretical signal zones for 90° range.

Lastly, if he is so placed on one of the four narrow lines at which the A and the N signals interlock with equal strength, he will receive only a steady dash, or monotone hum, of the so-called on-course.

Figure 5 further illustrates the signal pattern that will prevail for a typical range station whose four on-course zones are directed at 90° to one another. You will note that each quadrant may be considered to be roughly divided into one pure quadrant signal zone 30° wide and two bi-signal zones each 30° wide. The on-course zones proper are designed to have a width of approximately 3°. In actual practice, the apparent width of all zones will vary considerably from one station to another depending upon the directional pattern of the on-course zones and upon the volume level to which the pilot has adjusted his receiver.

In addition to the A and N signals, all radio range stations must send out identification signals so that a pilot may know to which station he is listening. These usually consist of two coded letters (such as CG—meaning Chicago). Such identification letters are sent each 30 seconds and consume a total time of 8 seconds. One set of identifications is sent first from the N antenna, while the A remains silent; the second from the A antenna, while the N remains silent. Thus, like the quadrant signals themselves, one identification only will be heard in the pure quadrant letter zones, two of unequal strength in the bi-signal zones, and two of equal strength in the on-course.

An additional signal zone is created by the identification signals, owing to the inability of the human ear to distinguish minute differences in signal strength between signals of the *same* type. This takes place in a very narrow zone, directly adjacent to the on-course and is termed the "twilight." Therein a pilot can distinguish a slight bi-signal indication rather than a pure on-course signal, but he is so close to the equal strength of identification signals that he cannot distinguish their difference in strength.

Directly over the range station itself is found a space shaped like an inverted cone in which no signal is heard; this is commonly termed the "cone of silence." This phenomenon is due to the cancellation of signals from opposing towers and provides the pilot with a means of locating the station. Figure 6 illustrates by two vertical cross sections the theoretical signal volume change that takes place as a pilot approaches and passes over a range station. It will be noted that the volume builds up rapidly near the station, drops to .zero over it, builds up rapidly after the station, and again decreases.

In practice, several factors alter cone of silence characteristics. As shown, at higher flight altitudes the cone is less abrupt and of greater duration. At high receiver volume

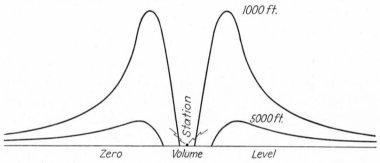

FIG. 6.—Theoretical volume-change pattern in vertical cross section near the range station. Note variation in cone width with variation in altitude above the station.

levels, the dead spot may be destroyed. Improper types of receiving antennas, "squeezing," and "bending" of range courses may also make detection of the cone very difficult.

Since the on-course zones of radio ranges are usually desired to be directed along established airways, it is often necessary to distort the range pattern from the 90° pattern discussed. This is termed "squeezing and bending the beams." This change is accomplished by various devices such as reducing the power from one antenna or absorbing a portion of the power from one single tower. In the first instance, a range will be squeezed as in Fig. 7, and in the second, one beam only will be bent or displaced, as in Fig. 8. Such distortion also changes the signal pattern to some extent, chiefly by increasing the width of the bi-signal zones in the wide quadrants and decreasing their width in the

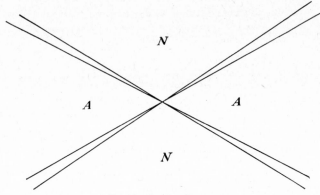

Fig. 7.—Squeezed range.

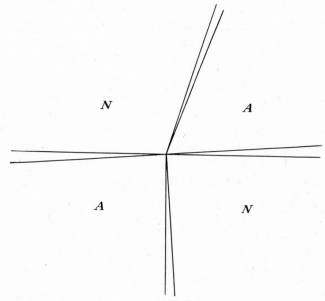

Fig. 8.—Station with one range course bent.

narrow quadrants. An appreciation of this change in field pattern is very important if orientation problems must be flown on such ranges.

RADIO RANGE ECCENTRICITIES

Although the far-flung network of radio ranges now existing in the United States is unquestionably the finest system of air navigational aids yet placed in service, radio ranges of the present low-frequency type are far from perfect in performance. While flying them, many of the following troubles must be expected.

Static.—Low-frequency wave bands are subject to severe static disturbances, both during thunderstorm activity and while flying through rain or snow.

Fading and Skip.—Two types of radio wave are sent out from low-frequency stations—ground wave and sky wave. Under normal conditions, the signals from such stations are predominantly from the ground wave traveling nearly horizontal to the earth. Occasionally, however, the sky wave (which normally travels sharply away from the earth's surface) is reflected earthward intermittently and causes the signals to fluctuate in volume or be displaced from their correct position. Often a far distant station on the same frequency may overpower one near by.

Bent and Shifted Beams.—Very often metallic ores in the earth, mountainous terrain, or large bodies of metals (such as city buildings) may cause one or more of the beams to be bent, instead of forming a straight on-course, or to be shifted from their published positions. Stations located on or near tidewater frequently are directionally unstable.

Multiple Courses.—Mountainous terrain and metallic deposits frequently split beams into multiple courses. Then, instead of one on-course sector, a pilot will discover several, such as shown in Fig. 9. So very erratic is this phenomenon that no sure rule can be used to decide which is the true on-course.

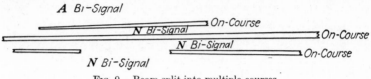

FIG. 9.—Beam split into multiple courses.

Swinging Beams.—Occasionally some range stations are characterized by "swinging." This type of range is extremely difficult to follow since the on-course moves from side to side and makes it almost impossible to obtain and keep a steady compass heading either to or from the station.

False Cones.—Actually, false cones of silence do not exist. However, unless a pilot uses proper receiver volume (reasonably low) when nearing the station and, *in addition, checks the complete volume sequence* of the cone, he may be misled by momentary fades in volume into thinking he has passed over the station. Such false cones never have the true volume-change sequence of the real cone.

ADDITIONAL RADIO AIDS TO NAVIGATION

In conjunction with the radio ranges several other types of radio navigational aids are used along the airways. The main purpose of these is to assist the pilot in obtaining definite "fixes" of position at points intermediate between the range stations.

Among the most important of these supplementary aids are the following types of radio markers:

M Type Marker.—These are low-powered, nondirectional radio stations usually placed at points along the airways where a pilot should retune his receiver from one radio range station to the next on his course. They transmit merely a single code letter approximately every 5 seconds and on the frequencies of both adjacent ranges. Normally they may be heard approximately 5 miles either side of their location. Such marker stations maintain a listening watch on the company frequencies of the airlines which pass over them, as well as on 3105 (and some on 6210) kilocycles which is the non-scheduled aircraft frequency. They may transmit to aircraft on either 278 kilocycles or on the frequency of the adjacent radio ranges.

Z Type Marker.—Because of the fact that the cone of silence does not always provide a positive and reliable means of determining the exact position of a radio range station, so-called Z type markers are installed at almost all radio range stations for this purpose. These operate on an ultra-high frequency of 75 megacycles (75,000 kilocycles) and send out a small inverted cone-shaped signal field directly above the range station. Owing to the high frequency used, a special receiver must be installed for their reception. Upon passing over a Z type marker, the pilot is furnished a positive check, both visually and aurally; the first by means of a small light on the instrument panel which reaches maximum brilliance directly over the station, and the second by a steady high-pitched signal which likewise reaches maximum intensity over the station. Like the cone of silence, the duration of the Z type marker indication increases with increasing flight altitude.

Fan-type Marker.—These are also high-frequency markers operating on 75 megacycles and are used as position markers on the beams of certain radio ranges. Their chief value is in conjunction with range stations serving congested traffic areas, such as New York and Chicago. One such marker is usually placed on each beam of the range at some desirable distance from the station, such as 20 to 25 miles, and is used to facilitate traffic control about the station. In addition, they provide the pilot with a positive check on his distance from the station, and by means of a coded signal, identify the beam.   All fan markers use the following code system:

The marker on the first beam clockwise from true north transmits one dash.

That on the second beam clockwise from true north, two dashes.

Those on the third and fourth beams. three and four dashes, respectively.

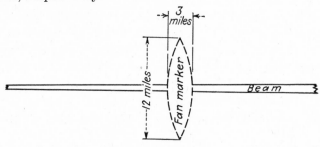

Fig. 10.—Fan marker.   Horizontal cross section at approximately 3000 feet.

Like the Z type marker, they are received both visually and aurally, although their signal is of the interrupted type rather than steady.   Figure 10 illustrates their shape in horizontal cross section.

In addition to markers, fixes along an airway may be obtained wherever any two beams of two range stations intersect.   If equipped with two receivers, it is a simple matter to tune one receiver to the frequency of each station and so obtain a fix where the on-courses intersect.   If equipped with only one receiver, the best procedure is to establish a gyro or compass heading that will ensure following the beam of the range being flown.   Thereafter, the receiver may be tuned to the frequency of the intersecting station until the on-course is crossed.

In the foregoing brief presentation of radio navigational aids, no attempt has been made to set forth more than the necessary highlights on the subject.   Before attempting any actual range flying, considerable detailed information must be obtained by any pilot regarding the specific ranges he expects to use. He should investigate the range frequencies, the courses of the beams (always given as magnetic courses computed at the station), location of A and N quadrants, identification signals, location of the station with respect to the airport, etc. Most of this detailed information is shown on the sectional airway charts published by the Federal government. These are frequently revised as the radio range network warrants it. Throughout such an extensive range network as exists in the United States, however, numerous changes are constantly taking place. Notice of such changes is made immediately over the C.A.A. teletype system and is available to all concerned. Also, weekly and monthly summaries are published and may be obtained upon request.

CHAPTER III

BEAM TECHNIQUES

Flying the radio ranges may well be considered an art and, as in the execution of any art, the technique and finesse of the performer invariably stamps him as amateur or professional. Unfortunately in range flying, too large a percentage of pilots—including professional pilots—label themselves as amateurs by their lack of appreciation of the necessity for sound technique. All too often, the average pilot is satisfied with haphazard beam flying as long as he accomplishes his basic purpose in reaching a destination.

This attitude shows a failure to appreciate the possible advantages obtained from a sure and smooth technique. Some of these are a saving of time and gasoline, an increased measure of passenger comfort, and most important, an increased measure of safety due to sure rather than haphazard navigation. For the achievement of this latter point alone, any efforts spent in perfecting range-flying technique are worth many times the effort involved.

Although it is probable that the pilot with the amateur's attitude may fly the ranges without serious difficulties, unquestionably he will always be more prone to error under adverse circumstances than a pilot who "knows the answers." In other words, it is the amateurish range flyer who becomes confused and thus lost.

If there were no such thing as wind, flying the radio ranges would be simplicity itself. The only requisites then would be a good compass and the necessary maps showing the location of the radio range stations and the courses of their beams.

Any pilot under such circumstances could steer a course to a desired beam and thereafter fly it by maintaining its published course. It will also be apparent, however, if there were no such thing as wind, radio ranges themselves would be unnecessary for navigation.

Illogical as it may seem, many pilots attempt to execute their beam flying without proper consideration of wind and its drifting effect. They seem to think of a beam as a railroad track; for when once on it, they attempt to use the published course as if it were a pair of rails. Even though serious difficulties do not always arise from such a conception of beam flying, the resultant zigs and zags that are made as the pilot haphazardly tries to reconcile the airplane's heading with that of the beam preclude anything but the label of amateur.

CONVERGENCE ON BEAMS

Probably one of the most valuable assets that a pilot can achieve in flying radio ranges is a proper appreciation of angles. When he is able to visualize the angle that any heading he may fly will make with the beam course, he has accomplished one half of a necessary mental combination. The other half is in interpreting the change in character of the signals into angular value as he flies headings to or from the beam.

To clarify these two statements, refer to Fig. 11. It will be apparent from this that if a pilot is receiving a pure N signal, as at point X, and wishes to intersect the east beam ($270°$ toward the station), he must assume some heading that will converge on the beam at greater than $30°$. This should be evident from the signal alone and a proper appreciation of the range pattern.

Since the bi-signal zone is $30°$ wide and his position is outside it, he cannot possibly reach the east beam with less than a $30°$ angle; and since the signal places him anywhere within

an additional 30° beyond the bi-signal zone, he probably
would be *certain* to intersect the east beam only by flying at
right angles to it (0°). Such a course will also be the most

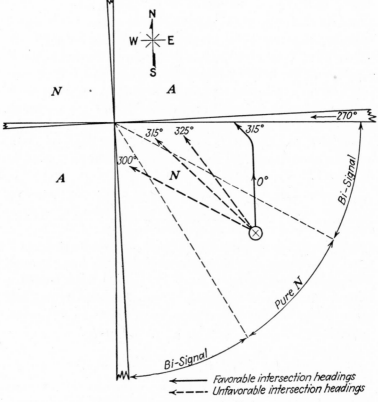

Fig. 11.—Beam intersection.

favorable he can choose under unknown wind conditions.
This might be considered as playing the averages in his favor.

Now, on the assumption that he has elected to fly at right
angles to the beam (heading 0), it will be seen that this heading should undergo change before the on-course is reached;
otherwise, it will carry him right through the beam at too

large an angle and necessitate a large amount of turn in order to come back to it. In such a situation, the second requisite —namely, the appreciation of signal change—is invaluable. In this instance, the pilot should be able to follow with some degree of accuracy his approach to the on-course by the changing character of the signals. As he enters the bi-signal zone, he will begin to pick up the background of the on-course very faintly. It will grow steadily louder in relation to the N signal. At the halfway point, the background will be one-half as strong as the N. Sometime thereafter, and before he reaches the pure on-course, it would be desirable to change his angle to the beam in order to converge at an angle of about 45° (heading 315). Then, when the beam is intersected, fewer turns and of less magnitude will be needed to follow it.

The preceding example is only one of many that might be given to illustrate the importance of appreciating angular values in relation to signals and signal change. Considerable assistance will be gained by laying out other radio range patterns and diagraming imaginary flight paths from various locations. Necessarily, however, only long and intensive radio range flying will build up a proper appreciation of the signal changes. For this type of work, the Link Trainer is without equal.

BEAM BRACKETING

In previous paragraphs, the importance of proper methods for converging on a desired beam were set forth. Even more important is the necessity for proper technique of flying the beam once it has been intersected.

Much difference of opinion exists as to how a beam should be flown. A brief analysis of the situation is desirable. Although a beam course is published as an exact number of degrees, such as 270 (magnetic, computed at the station), the beam in reality is 3° wide, or 1½° either side of the published course. This is an important consideration when it comes to following it; since, diverging at the rate of 3° away from the station, any beam will soon attain an appreciable width (1½ miles at 30 miles from the station, etc.).

This fact should make it clear that it is impractical to attempt flying the center of a beam or a pure on-course signal. The reason is that the width of the on-course allows too great a variation of heading without any indication as to whether the flight path is in alignment with the beam. Flying a beam in such fashion invariably results in a zigzag progress from one side of the beam to the other until, nearing the station, a series of rapid corrections is at last necessary to find the correct heading. Naturally, the greater the drift, the more exaggerated this pattern will become.

The desirable manner in which to fly a beam is on the edge —preferably, the right edge to conform to traffic rules. Flying the edge also provides a positive means of ascertaining the exact heading necessary to make good the beam course. This is due to the fact that the edge of a beam is defined by difference in signal—on the one side, a pure on-course, on the other side, a shade of off-course. It is evident, then, that an edge having no width in theory provides a directional line that is not available when flying the full on-course signal.

By assuming that it has been decided to fly the right edge of a beam, some procedure should be followed to arrive at the proper heading to make good the beam course. As has been brought out previously, no complications would exist if it were not for wind drift. Since in almost all instances wind and its drifting effect does complicate flying a beam, a simple procedure, termed "beam bracketing," should be followed (refer to Fig. 12).

In the following examples, it will be assumed that the published beam course is 270° toward the station and that the wind in all instances is unknown. Figure 12a illustrates a simple beam bracket as it would work out if no drift were present. The beam would be approached at an angle of 45° by flying 315°. This heading should be held until the *opposite* off-course signal is received on the far side of the beam. Thereafter, a turn is made to the left in order to return toward the on-course at an angle of about 20° (heading 250). At the first on-course signal, a turn is made to the right in order to leave the beam at approximately 20° (heading 290). If each of these headings, the one *on* and the other *off* the beam, produce the desired results promptly, the pilot has established a so-called bracket, or angle, 40° wide, within which his final heading must lie. Subsequently, he must narrow this bracket. Following this same method, he returns to the on-course at a 10° angle (heading 260) and then flies 10° off course (heading 280). Now he has achieved a 20° bracket.

If the on and off course reactions have been approximately of the same time interval, it is safe for him to assume that a desired final heading will lie very close to the middle of this latter bracket. By returning again to the on-course and adjusting his heading to approximately 270° at the very edge, he should find that he can hold the edge by not over a plus or minus 3° change from 270. Since it is practically impossible to fly even a gyro heading more accurately than to 2°, he has established his final heading with sufficient accuracy for practical purposes. Any slight corrections that may be needed will be instantly indicated as long as he follows the beam edge.

Beamed Bracketing with Timed Turns.—In the above explanation, use of a directional gyro has been presumed since it is almost a prerequisite for smooth and accurate beam flying. It is perfectly feasible, however, to bracket a beam with only a turn indicator and clock. Accurately timed, standard rate turns (3 degrees per second) are the essential factor. The bracketing procedure is similar to that of using a gyro except for the way in which it must be mentally worked out. As an example, let us assume the same bracket is worked out with a turn and bank indicator as has been previously explained by Fig. 12*a*.

Again, let the beam (270°) be intersected at an angle of approximately 45°. Upon reaching the opposite off-course signal on the far side of the beam, a timed turn to the left would be made for approximately 22 seconds (65°) in order to establish a 20° closing angle toward the on-course. Upon receiving the first on-course signal, a turn is made to the right of approximately 13 seconds (40°) in order to leave the beam at a 20° angle. These two turns, the one left and the other right, on and off the beam, should set up the original bracketing angle of 40° in the same manner as is done with a gyro. Thereafter, this original bracketing angle is progressively reduced by timed turns of less duration until the edge of the beam can be flown with corrections of not more than 2 or 3 seconds of turn.

It should be appreciated that accuracy of headings achieved by timed turns will be uncertain. Likewise, when an airplane is turning almost continuously, a magnetic compass is practically useless to check the heading. With this in mind, it is always well when using timed turns to set up an initial bracketing angle of somewhat larger size than when using a gyro (instead of 40°, make it at least 60°). It is better to take a few more turns in working out the bracket than to miss the beam completely. Also, it cannot be overemphasized that proper signal interpretation is just as essential as when using a gyro.

Drift Conditions.—Figure 12*b* illustrates how this same procedure works under drift conditions. Again the beam is approached and intersected on a heading of 315°. Thereafter, since the drift is still unknown, an angle of 20° to the published beam heading is again taken in order to return to it (heading 250). If there is a cross wind producing drift to the right, this heading of 250 may not be sufficient to effect a return to the beam (if 20° of drift exists). The pilot will

soon become aware of this as he continues to receive an
off-course signal rather than returning to the on-course.

This should soon tell him two things: that he has a wind
from the left which is tending to drift him away from the

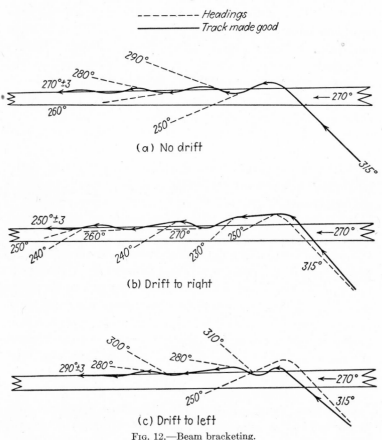

Fig. 12.—Beam bracketing.

beam, and that he must alter his heading still more in the direction of the beam in order to return to it. First, he may
take 240°, and finding that his return is extremely slow, go to
230°. Provided that this latter heading returns him to the
beam, he then corrects to the right in order to leave it again.

This time he should appreciate that he can no longer turn to 290 but must assume some heading such as 270 and allow the drift to take him off the beam. If he finds that a heading of 230 is required to reach the on-course, and then 270 is sufficient to again return off course, he has established his original bracket with these two headings as the limits. Once again he must reduce this original bracket by taking headings on and off the edge that will constantly reduce the angle in the same manner as in the previous example. If 20° of drift does exist, his final heading will resolve to approximately 250°.

Figure 12c illustrates how the same procedure should work out with a wind from the right which tends to drift him toward the beam. Under this condition, he will find that the original 20° angle returning to the beam will be too great and the wind will tend to drift him immediately into the center of the on-course. A prompt appreciation and reaction to this situation is essential if he is to remain on the right side of the beam. Then he should at once assume a right correction off the beam of greater than 290°, such as 300 or 310. Once off, a heading of 270 or 280 should be sufficient so that the drift will return him to the on-course. These headings will establish an original bracket between 310 and 280; as in the previous examples, he must reduce it to arrive at a final heading. If we assume that a 20° drift to the left exists, the final heading would be approximately 290.

Summary.—In all the foregoing explanations of beam bracketing, specific angles and headings have been used merely for the sake of clarity and to emphasize a *procedure*. Bracketing a beam is not done by formula but rather by working from such a *basic* procedure as outlined and *adapting* its general principles to the specific problem. Reduced to a minimum this procedure advocates the following:

1. The beam edge should be used as a directional indication rather than the full width of the on-course.

2. Since wind drift can always be assumed to exist, some systematic method must be used to determine the heading necessary to make good the beam course.

3. The simplest system is to fly on and off the edge of the beam at sufficient angles to set up a so-called bracket within which the final heading must lie.

4. The original bracket having been established, it must be reduced by flying on and off the edge of the beam at decreasing angles until a final heading is achieved.

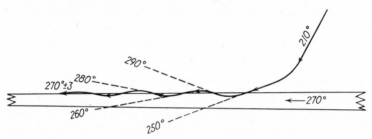

Fig. 13.—Beam bracketing.

5. This final heading should not be considered more accurate than a plus or minus 3° and should be constantly checked by attempting to maintain the beam edge.

Before leaving the subject of beam bracketing, several other points should be clarified.

In the examples furnished, it will be noted that the approach to the beam was in each instance made from the left side, thus necessitating a crossing of the beam before the bracket was started. This was necessary to work the bracket on the right edge. Crossing the beam in this manner naturally is not required if the initial approach is to be made from the right. Then the beam should be converged upon at an appropriate angle (previously discussed) until just prior to entering the on-course (twilight zone). At that point, the original 20° bracketing angle may be taken up (refer to Fig. 13).

First impressions of the bracketing procedure that has been outlined might admit the assumption that unnecessary turns are required that might be avoided by taking up the published beam course and following the on-course. This assumption is not true, however, in practice. Many more turns and changes of heading will invariably result with almost any other technique and, in addition, will take place at the most inopportune time—near the station.

As most experienced pilots will testify, the necessity for rapid corrections close to the station usually produces over-corrections and subsequent failure to hit the cone of silence. With the bracketing procedure outlined, the major corrective turns are completed soon after reaching the beam; and if the job is well done, no further corrections in excess of 2 or 3° should be needed.

As a final point, the obvious warning must be made that the success or failure of beam bracketing, as well as flying the beam after it is bracketed, lies in the ability of the individual pilot to *analyze skillfully* the signals he receives and to *react promptly* to them. To do this, a clear mental picture must be had of what is taking place, and more important, what is going to be done next.

In other words, a skillful beam pilot will always be mentally ahead of his problem. In this way only will he be able to react promptly and in the correct manner to the *first* change in signal. If he allows several signals to go by each time he turns off and on the beam, his whole bracket will be prolonged and made inaccurate. Obviously the development of a coordinated ear and mind is a matter of long and continuous practice.

PROCEDURE TURNS

Next in importance to proper procedures and techniques in flying the beam itself is the execution of a turn-around on a beam—commonly called "procedure turn." Of the numerous methods that have been advanced, one has gradually become commonly accepted (refer to Fig. 14a). In this example, the airplane is considered to be flying away from the station on the east beam. With no drift existing, the heading is 90°—the same as the beam course.

A procedure turn is executed by altering the airplane's heading 45° to the right (heading 135°—always computed from the beam course) and maintaining this new heading for one minute. Thereafter a 180° turn is made to the left and the new heading (315) held until the beam is crossed. Then a left turn is made toward the station and the right edge followed to it.

The foregoing example illustrates the *desired* pattern of a procedure turn. In still air conditions, this pattern will actually be achieved; under conditions of drift, however, procedure turns offer considerable opportunity for difficulties.

Analyzing the purposes of the procedure turn, it can be said to have two: (1) to allow a pilot to reverse his direction on a beam; and (2) while so doing, to make possible his return to the beam at approximately the same point and with the same angle as he left it. It will be evident that under still air conditions, shown by Fig. 14a, both these objectives are attained.

Figure 14b indicates what may happen under conditions of drift. In this instance, the airplane's heading is 80° in order to make good the 90° beam course, thus establishing a wind from the left. It should be appreciated that this drift correction to the left does not in itself establish a definite wind direction. It may be from any direction between the arrows labeled 1 and 2. Therefore, when the pilot changes heading 45° to the right to start the procedure turn, the wind can either become a tail wind (no drift) or a cross wind. In either situation, the normal procedure turn will be distorted. If the wind happens to act as a tail wind, the airplane will be carried too far off the beam in 1 minute, thereby making a slow

return.   The second condition is more serious in that the
wind may become a direct cross wind during the procedure

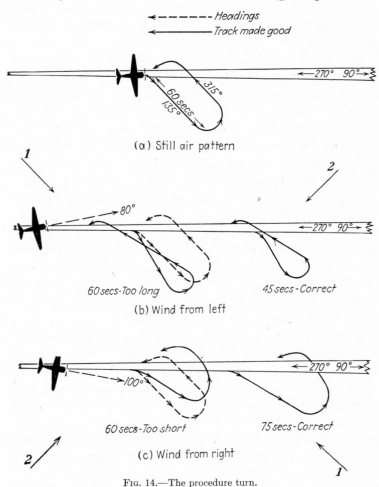

Fig. 14.—The procedure turn.

turn.   Then as the headings of 135° and 315° are flown off
and back to the beam, the actual track made good will be
distorted as shown by the solid line.   This distortion may
result in both a delayed return to the beam and loss of

beam length in which to bracket before reaching the station.

The solution of this whole situation is quite simple. It will be seen that as long as the wind is from the left before starting the procedure turn, its effect is to carry the airplane too far off the beam—either by increased speed with the tail wind or increased angle with the cross wind. This may be eliminated by reducing the normal time off the beam to less than 1 minute. Thus, although the pattern may be distorted, *reduction of time will lessen the amount of distortion*.

Figure 14c shows the reverse situation with a wind from the right while making a procedure turn. By following the same reasoning as was advanced above, it will be seen that a wind from the right will act as either a head wind or a cross wind, but in either instance will tend to crowd the procedure turn toward the beam. Then, in all probability, the pilot will find himself back across the beam before he has completed the 180° turn and far out of position for starting his return to the station. This is handled by increasing the length of time off the beam to more than a minute, say between 75 to 90 seconds.

High Drift Angles.—It should now be apparent from the preceding explanation that procedure turns may be made with little difficulty under *normal* drift conditions (up to 10 or 12°) simply by proper time allowance. Under drift conditions of 15° or more, the problem becomes more complicated. Then the time allowance must be altered even more drastically, and in addition, some attempt made to correct the headings to compensate for the drift (refer to Fig. 15a and b).

In Fig. 15a, a 25° drift correction is being made to the left in order to make good a 90° beam course. In this instance, it will be apparent that time reduction off the beam alone will be insufficient to fully compensate for the extreme distortion produced upon the procedure turn pattern by a direct cross wind of such magnitude. In this case, it would be better to turn approximately 30° off the published beam heading instead of 45, hold for 30 to 40 seconds, and complete the turnaround by making a left turn of 150° rather than 180°. By following such a procedure, a portion of the wind effect will

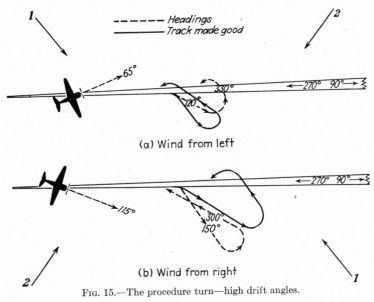

(a) Wind from left

(b) Wind from right

Fig. 15.—The procedure turn—high drift angles.

be taken care of by shortening the time and the remainder by altering the headings of the procedure turn.

Figure 15*b* illustrates this method applied to compensate for a strong wind from the right. Note that if the wind happens to act as a tail or head wind instead of a cross wind, the corrections applied will still not be harmful even though distorting the procedure pattern.

Although in the foregoing discussion it has been assumed that the wind direction is not known more accurately than as evidenced by the drift correction angle (wind from right or left of the beam), this is by no means the typical condition. Usually a pilot will know the wind direction and force with some degree of accuracy. Naturally this eliminates doubt as to whether the wind will act as a tail wind or cross wind during the procedure turn.

Note: Local traffic regulations often require that procedure turns be executed toward the left side of the beam rather than to the right. (La Guardia Field, New York, and Newark, New Jersey, require left procedures now.)

The method of execution is basically similar to the right procedure turn. In this case (assuming still air), the pilot makes his first 45° turn to the left off the beam, flies for 1 minute, and executes a 180° turn *to the right* to return to the beam. Upon reaching the on-course, however, the pilot should not cross the beam, but should begin immediately to bracket the right edge going in to the station.

VOLUME CONTROL

In many respects, it is unfortunate that range flying is by aural rather than visual signals, since the human ear is much more limited in sensitivity than the human eye. Its sensitivity is also impaired by changes in atmospheric pressure accompanying changes in altitude normal to flight. Furthermore, like the other human senses, aural acuteness differs widely in individuals.

It is not the purpose of this chapter to attempt to discuss so large a subject as the human ear in relation to range signals and flight. It is mentioned only in explanation of some of the generalities that must be used in discussing volume control. One of the most common faults of the average pilot flying range signals is improper use of volume control. By improper, it is not meant that volume is consistently carried at too high or too low a level, but rather that it is not controlled in a sensible manner.

Naturally, it is impossible for any two individuals with different aural sensitivity to agree on the terms high or low volume. What may be a comfortable level for the one may be unbearably high for the other; nevertheless, each individual can determine for himself what he considers low, moderate, and high volume levels. With this in mind, some remarks on volume control may be helpful.

As a general rule, the volume of signal that any individual should carry in the headphones is directly dependent upon which of two signal characteristics he is attempting to analyze:

1. Increase or decrease of signal strength as he flies closer to or farther from the transmitting station.

2. Change in signal character as he flies to or from an on-course zone.

Analyzing Volume Change.—Under this heading, two specific situations call for skillful use of the volume control. In many orientation methods, the first step is to ascertain which of two quadrants of similar signal the airplane is in. This is commonly done by assuming a predetermined course (forming the average bisector of both quadrants) which will either lead to or away from the station. The increase or decrease of station volume when such a course is flown will tell the pilot whether he is flying to or from the station, thus identifying the quadrant. For such detection of build-up or fade in signal strength, it is essential that a minimum volume be used for positive and rapid results.

A second important situation wherein change in station volume must be clearly recognized is upon the approach to the station itself. If it is assumed that the pilot has established himself on a beam and ascertained the proper heading, his remaining problem is to determine definitely when he has reached the station. If a high-frequency receiver is not available for picking up the Z marker, he must determine passing of the station by sharp changes in volume accompanied by the cone of silence. In order to do this, a low volume level must be used.

Actual technique should be generally as follows: After the beam course has been established and it is being followed to the station, the pilot should adjust his volume to a comfortable level, just sufficiently high to enable him to fly the beam accurately. Thereafter, he must maintain this same volume level throughout the approach to the station. The nearer the approach, the more frequently he will find it necessary to adjust the volume control. Just before the station itself, he will hear a distinct surge in volume, and over the station, the dead spot. Directly past the station, a second surge will be heard, followed by a rapid fade. High volume level usually results in destroying this characteristic volume pattern.

Analyzing Signal Change.—Under this heading, a pilot is primarily interested in determining the *change* in signal as he moves from one signal zone to another, or on and off the beam. This calls for at least moderate volume level so that the difference in signal character may be appreciated. Two primary situations exist. (1) When approaching a beam, sufficient volume must be had so that the change from a pure quadrant signal toward the on-course may be closely followed. (2) When working to bracket a beam, it is essential that the change from on-course to off-course be readily recognized.

In concluding this presentation of radio range flying techniques, it should be obvious that no attempt has been made to cover all phases of the subject. Four fundamental techniques only have been selected for a reasonably detailed explanation. These form the basis for successful and precise range work, and if properly mastered, go far toward eliminating the amateur's troubles.

CHAPTER IV

ORIENTATION METHODS

Radio range orientation may be considered a process of reascertaining an airplane's position by radio signals after it has once been lost. Although technically a position is never known precisely from radio signals except over a definite radio fix, a practical viewpoint allows a pilot to consider himself orientated as long as position is known with respect to a definite radio range beam with reasonable accuracy. From the foregoing statement, it will be apparent that the phrase, *reasonable accuracy*, is one that will always be interpreted differently. In other words, it is difficult to lay down any rule that will definitely distinguish the point at which a pilot becomes lost. For instance, a pilot using radio range signals for cross-country navigation can consider himself orientated as long as he is able to maintain his desired ground track and check it at frequent intervals. On the other hand, the pilot becomes definitely lost whenever he has failed to make good his desired ground track and is unable to prove his position by any of the navigational means at his disposal. Obviously, no sharp line can be drawn between these two conditions, but rather the first will shade gradually into the second. A pilot is seldom completely orientated at one moment and completely lost the next. Usually he will be lost somewhat in advance of his realization of it. In the discussion of radio-orientation methods to follow, it will be assumed in all instances that position is *definitely* unknown.

Starting from an unknown position with respect to any radio range station, it is equally difficult to lay down any rule making clear cut the point at which reorientation is completed. Offhand impressions may lead to the assumption that it is complete when the quadrant and direction of the

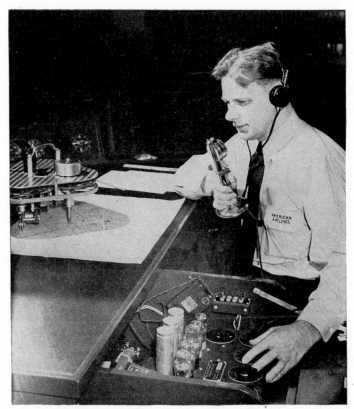

Checking the pilot—Link Trainer. (*Courtesy of American Airlines, Inc.*)

station are known. Such an assumption might be correct were it not for the incalculable effect of unknown wind or other conditions which probably were responsible for the pilot's becoming lost originally. For this reason, it is safer not to consider any orientation completed until a known beam has been reached and a course established on it.

Radio orientation may be simple or complex, depending upon numerous factors such as the type of radio equipment available, the clarity and accuracy of the radio signals received, and the effect of wind. Numerous methods for orientation have been worked out and proved in practice. Although all these are workable, no single method is the solution for all problems. Each method has its particular virtues and weaknesses. Thus, it is not enough for a pilot to know only one method of orientation. Probably a minimum of three or four should be clearly understood so that the proper one may be used in any given circumstance.

RADIO RANGE CHARTS

For radio range navigation, a pilot should properly equip himself with two types of charts. For ordinary cross-country navigation, the usual regional or sectional airways charts are sufficient. For problems being worked on specific stations such as instrument let-down procedures and orientation procedures, individual charts should be available for each station. These are usually drawn showing one or two range stations and their immediate vicinity. They are constructed on a large enough scale to show terrain characteristics and obstructions. In addition, such charts should show the so-called average bisector courses of the radio range quadrants (refer to sample radio range chart of El Paso in pocket on back cover).

An average bisector course may be defined as that course (or its reciprocal) which forms the average between the courses bisecting quadrants of the same signal. Referring to Fig. 16, it will be seen that the course bisecting the north N quadrant may be computed as 352° and that of the south N quadrant as 5°. By taking an average between these two, we may compute an average bisector for both quadrants as 358°. For convenience in the use of average bisectors, they are usually drawn as shown in Fig. 16 as two courses figured toward the station, one being the reciprocal of the other.

Rather than computing the courses mathematically, it is more expedient and fully as practical to determine the average bisectors by inspection. On the chart of the range station

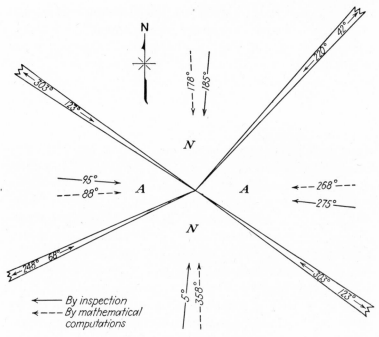

Fig. 16.—Average bisectors.

in question, select the pair of quadrants, either A or N, containing the narrowest quadrant. Using a transparent straight edge passed through the station, select the *one* line that most nearly divides both quadrants. In the selection, favor the narrowest quadrant. Rather than a single line, however, draw in the average bisectors as explained previously and determine their values to the nearest 5° by a protractor. Thereafter construct the bisectors for the other pair of quadrants at 90° from the first pair. Although none of the quadrants may be perfectly bisected, the average bisector courses constructed in this manner will be practical.

90° ORIENTATION SYSTEM

The 90° system is one of many orientation methods that may be used with airplanes equipped with nondirectional receiving antennas. Referring to Fig. 17, the detailed steps are as follows:

1. After tuning in the proper radio range station, the type of signal being received should be analyzed, *i.e.*, whether it is a pure A, a pure N, or a bi-signal A or N.

2. From the radio range chart, determine the two bisector courses which are at *right angles* to the bisectors of the quadrants in which the airplane may be. In other words, if the airplane is in one of the N quadrants, select the bisectors of the A quadrants as those to be used.

3. Of the two chosen bisectors, turn the airplane to the one that is nearer to the present heading. Referring to the figure, it will be seen that if the heading at the start of the problem is 40°, the 110° A bisector will be used. At this point, it should be recognized that the airplane can intersect only one of *two* beams of the range, the northeast or the southeast.

4. While flying the 110° heading, carefully analyze any signal change. If the problem is started within a bi-signal zone, as any of the four points shown in the figure, a signal change should soon be evident. From starting points 1 and 2, the airplane will be flying away from the nearer pair of beams and the background of the on-course will gradually fade out. In these instances, the pilot should make a 180° turn and restart his problem, using the 290° bisector. This will save time by allowing the pilot to work the problem on the closer beams. From points 3 and 4, the change in signal received

will indicate that the closer pair of beams is being approached and the 110° heading should be continued.

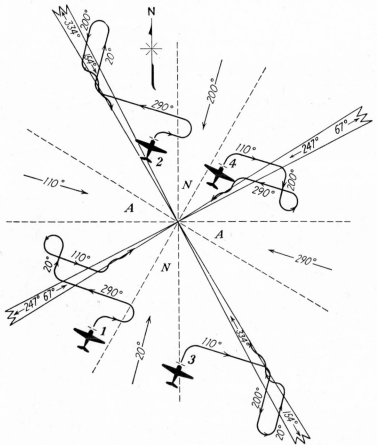

Fig. 17.—Ninety-degree orientation.

5. Continue the proper bisector heading until one of the two possible beams has been intersected.

6. At the *first* off-course signal after passing through the beam, make a 90° right turn. Since this new heading will always be one of the bisectors printed on the range chart, it

should be selected before the beam is intersected so that it may be assumed without delay.

7. After flying this new heading until the beam is definitely left behind, the pilot can determine which of the two beams he has crossed. By referring to the figure and assuming that the airplane has started from either position 3 or 4, the problem will be solved as follows: If the southeast beam has been crossed, the heading assumed after the 90° right turn will carry the airplane back across the beam and again into the N quadrant. If the start has been made from position 4, this heading will continue to take the airplane away from the northeast beam and into the A quadrant. By determining which one of these two signal changes has taken place, the pilot knows which beam he has crossed.

8. Having identified the beam, the next step is simply to return to it. In all cases similar to 2 and 3, the pilot will be orientated immediately upon crossing the beam the *second* time. He should, however, continue this heading off the beam for approximately one minute before attempting to return to it. A 180° left turn is then made and this new heading held until the right side of the beam is reached. Thereafter, the edge of the beam is bracketed and followed to the station. In all instances similar to 1 and 4, the airplane will continue to leave the beam after the 90° right turn is made. In all probability, by the time the pilot can decide from the signal change which of the two beams he has crossed, the airplane will be sufficiently distant from the beam to allow a turn being made immediately. In this instance, a 270° left turn should be made in order to return to the beam.

It will be seen that the 90° system basically is a progressive elimination of three beams. Like all orientation systems, however, in practice it is fully as important to recognize its advantages and limitations, as it is to know the procedure itself. Some essential advantages are:

1. It can be successfully flown by a pilot with limited experience in analyzing radio signals.

2. It is usually a fairly rapid system when the starting point is within a bi-signal zone and always is completed with the airplane flying toward the station.

3. All headings flown are bisectors, printed on the map.

4. It is the *only* system other than loop orientation which can be successfully completed without the use of fades or builds of signal. It is based upon signal rather than volume change; therefore it is definitely advantageous whenever static or other atmospheric conditions interfere with reception.

Some of the major disadvantages are:

1. It is unfavorable to use if the starting point is in a pure signal zone. Nevertheless, since the bi-signal zones form approximately 60 per cent of any quadrant, it is useful about two-thirds of the time.

2. In quadrants of more than 90° between beams, the system is likely to be very slow and perhaps entirely impossible to work under unfavorable wind conditions.

3. Under high wind conditions, the distortion of the 90° system pattern may be serious. For this reason, extreme care should always be taken to definitely prove the results of each course flown and avoid hasty decisions.

FADE-OUT PARALLEL SYSTEM

The fade-out parallel system of orientation is only one of many systems based upon flying quadrant bisectors to obtain either a build-up or fade of signal volume for quadrant identification. The detailed procedure is as follows:

1. Having tuned in the proper radio range station, determine the type of signal being received. Referring to Fig. 18, it will be assumed that a bi-signal N is being received at the start of the problem, the airplane being thus placed in either N quadrant.

2. At the start, assume a heading parallel to the course of the N quadrant bisector nearest to the heading of the airplane. For example, assume the 170° bisector course is used.

Flying such a heading, it will be apparent that the airplane will move closer to the station if starting in the north N

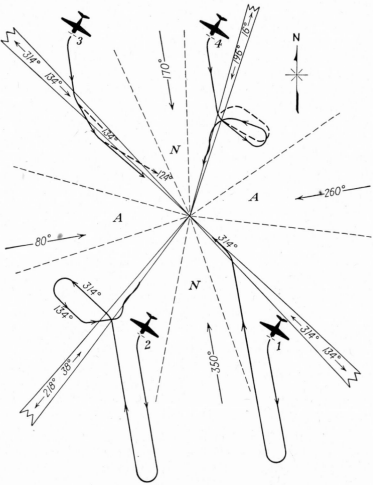

Fig. 18.—Fadeout parallel orientation.

quadrant and farther from the station if in south N quadrant.

3. Now decrease the signal volume received in the headphones to a minimum *readable* level (just sufficient for recog-

nition of any possible *signal change*). Continue on this bisector course *not less* than 2 minutes before making a definite decision as to change in signal volume. Often more time will be needed. If a fade is received, make a 180° turn and fly parallel to the reciprocal bisector course. On this course, a build-up in volume should confirm the fact that the airplane is now flying toward the station. Referring to Fig. 18, it will be evident that such a signal volume sequence would place the airplane in the south N quadrant.

4. Having proved the starting quadrant, continue the inbound bisector heading until one of the two beams bounding the quadrant is intersected.

5. Before reaching a beam, the pilot should decide which of the two possible ones he would prefer to follow and, at the very moment of reaching an on-course, turn the airplane stationward on the published course of this preferred beam.

6. One of two things will happen. The plane will either remain in the on-course (or very close to it) or it will go through the beam and move off course toward an open quadrant. In Fig. 18, if the pilot decided to parallel the southeast beam, the two possible situations are illustrated.

7. In the first case, it would be necessary merely to properly bracket the beam and continue toward the station. In the second case, a 180° turn should be made *away* from the station and the new heading assumed toward the beam. Usually this new heading should be altered just prior to reaching the on-course so that the bracketing process may be started from a reduced angle.

In practice, the fade-out parallel proves a fairly rapid method of orientation under normal conditions. Nevertheless, it has some disadvantages:

1. Under erratic signal conditions, flying for builds or fades of signal volume is not always easy or trustworthy. A strong head wind may decrease ground speed to such an extent that a fade or build will not be evident on the bisector course taken

originally. If such a situation exists, the reciprocal bisector course will usually give rapid results.

2. Strong cross winds may drift the airplane seriously from the bisector course. Also starting positions in the bi-signal zones of an extremely wide quadrant are unfavorable for proving builds and fades.

3. Wind drift can often confuse a pilot after he has assumed a heading parallel to the beam course. Even though he may be flying the course of the beam which he has intersected, wind drift may lead him to think he has intersected the opposite beam. Referring to Fig. 18, a method is shown for reducing the probability of such error due to drift. From starting point 3, it will be assumed that an easterly wind tends to drift the airplane off the northwest beam after the parallel has been taken up. By immediately altering the heading 10 or 15° toward the beam, the drift effect will likely be so diminished as to cause no trouble. Furthermore, if the start had been made from position 4, the application of this correction angle would not alter the signal change received.

THE TRUE FADE-OUT SYSTEM

With the exception of loop orientation, the true fade-out method can probably be considered the most positive procedure for orientation in that it may be used successfully on almost any type of range pattern. Referring to Fig. 19, the procedure is as follows:

1. Having tuned in the proper range station, the pilot proceeds to determine which quadrant he is in by flying parallel to quadrant bisectors for a build or fade. The detailed steps are exactly similar to those outlined for the fade-out parallel system.

2. Having determined the quadrant, the bisector course toward the station should be followed until a beam is intersected. By assuming that the problem has started in the east A quadrant, either the southeast or northeast beam can be intersected.

3. Continue through the on-course, and upon receiving the *first* off-course signal on the far side, start a standard rate (3 degrees per second) left turn which should be continued until

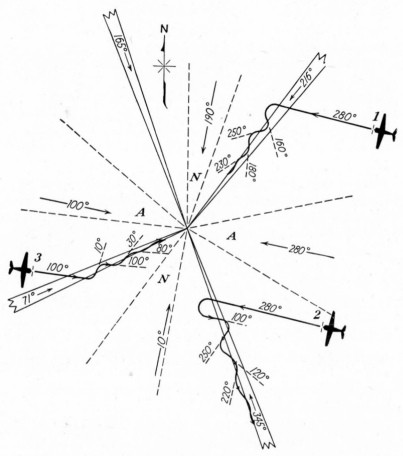

Fig. 19.—True fadeout orientation.

either the on-course is again reached or 180° of turn completed. If a 180° turn is made before returning to the on-course, do not turn farther, but hold this new heading until the on-course is reached. In either case, note carefully the heading at which the turn is completed.

4. At the time of starting the left turn, make a mental note of the signal being received (either an A or an N). Throughout the remainder of the problem, this same off-course signal should always be kept to the *right*. *Remembering this rule will eliminate confusion of signals.*

5. *Immediately* the left turn has again contacted the on-course, begin a right turn. This should be continued until the same off-course signal is again received or until reaching the original bisector course. Note carefully the heading at which the turn is stopped.

6. These first two turns serve merely to establish a large angle or bracket within which the beam course must lie (refer to Fig. 19). Thereafter, the problem resolves to one of reducing the size of this original bracketing angle by a series of alternate left and right turns on and off the beam. This portion of the problem is similar to the bracketing process explained in Chap. III, with the exception that an unknown beam makes it necessary to start with a large bracketing angle rather than a small one. A careful study of this figure will illustrate this fact.

7. Although no exact rule can specify how rapidly the original bracketing angle can be reduced by subsequent headings, a rough guide may be used. Not more than 30° can safely be taken off either side of the original angle. If, as in position 3, it is a small angle to start with, 30° will probably be excessive. Likewise, as the bracket grows smaller, subsequent reduction must be careful until the beam heading is finally established.

8. After the beam has been bracketed and the heading to hold it established, the beam may or may not be completely identified. Final identification should always be made by listening for either a build or fade in signal volume. Unless this is done, it would be easy to confuse the northeast and southeast beams in Fig. 19 under unknown drift conditions.

9. It will be noted from Fig. 19 that the orientation pro-

cedure produces a 50 per cent chance that the airplane will be flying away from the station while the beam is being identified. In this instance, after identification a procedure turn should be made in order to return toward the station.

The true fade-out method possesses several distinctive features:

1. It provides a sure method of identifying the beam while simultaneously establishing the heading to fly it.

2. If the system is correctly followed and no assumptions are made before the beam is completely identified, it proves the most certain method of establishing a beam heading under high drift conditions.

3. It may be used advantageously in all except very narrow quadrants.

Some disadvantages are:

1. Under certain conditions it may be impossible to identify a quadrant by a build or fade in volume.

2. Near the station large turns are undesirable and often the beam may not be bracketed before the station is passed. In this case, it would be preferable to use the parallel system.

3. Another objection applicable to large transport-type airplanes is the number and magnitude of the turns involved. However, if these are made at the standard rate, such an objection is minimized.

OTHER SYSTEMS

The three orientation systems explained thus far can be considered the basic orientation systems for use with an airplane that is not equipped with a direction-finding loop antenna. As has been noted, each of these systems has certain inherent weaknesses that may prove troublesome if an attempt is made to use the system on a range unsuited to it. However, if a pilot is familiar with all three systems and uses care to select the proper one for the type of range station he is flying, he should be able to orientate on any type of range station without difficulty.

Numerous other methods of orientation exist, however. Most of these are either a combination or a special adaptation of the three basic systems described.

Close-in Parallel System.—In Fig. 20 the so-called "close-in" parallel system is diagramed. This modification of the parallel system previously explained is very convenient to use whenever a beam is intersected very close to the range station. For example:

Assume that a pilot has started an orientation procedure from an open A quadrant zone on a range station of the type shown. Deciding perhaps to work a fade-out parallel orientation, he starts out by flying parallel to the 270° A bisector for a build-up or fade-out in signal volume.

Soon an increase in signal volume informs him that he is progressing toward the station from the east A quadrant and will intersect either the northeast or southeast beam. Normally, at this point he would decide which of the two possible beam courses he will adopt upon reaching the on-course signal.

However, as in this example, the starting point in the quadrant or wind may have determined that the flight path will be such that a beam is intersected very close to the range station. The pilot will first become aware of this situation when a very rapid change of signal takes place as he flies through the narrow bi-signal zone near the station. Very possibly he may fly completely through a beam or even two beams before he is able to react to the change in signal.

Such a rapid signal change can indicate only one thing— the flight path has intersected a beam or beams very close to the range station. Usually the faster and more complex the signal change, the closer has been this intersection.

Confronted with such a situation, a pilot must discard all preconceived plans he may have made up to this point. First, being so close to the station it will be almost impossible to work a basic orientation system such as the fade-out parallel, true fade-out, or 90° since the signal changes will occur too rapidly to allow intelligent reactions. Secondly,

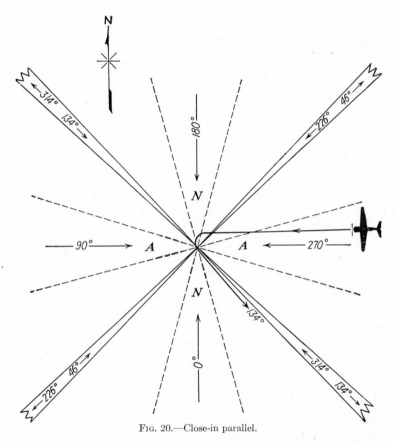

Fig. 20.—Close-in parallel.

knowing he is close to the station should inform a pilot that he is no longer "lost." His only real difficulty now is to choose a beam and get on it. To do this, proceed generally as follows:

1. *Immediately* it is recognized that a beam or beams have been crossed very close to the station, choose the *outbound*

course of *any one* of the four beams and adopt this as a heading. *Do not go back to a bisector heading.* Usually it is most expedient to select the outbound beam course that may be reached with the least amount of turning. In Fig. 20, the pilot is assumed to have started a left turn after reaching the northeast beam and he simply continued this until a heading parallel to the southeast beam was reached. Note that during the turn he went through two other beams in addition to the northeast beam originally intersected. This may easily happen before a pilot can choose which heading to settle down on.

2. Having selected a heading parallel to one of the beam courses, reduce the signal volume and fly this same heading until a decrease of signal volume proves that the station is being left behind. Normally this should take less than 2 minutes.

3. At this point, there should be little further confusion as to position. It is known that the flight path is away from the station and parallel to the outbound heading of a beam. The A or N quadrant signal being received will determine whether the flight path is to the right or left of the beam. Thereafter, simply turn toward the beam and bracket it going away from the station until far enough out to make a procedure turn.

Fade-out Right-angle System.—In Fig. 21 the fade-out right-angle system of orientation is illustrated. It will be apparent that this method is also only a special adaptation of the fade-out parallel system. It is designed for use with a 90° range pattern or in the narrow quadrants of a squeezed range. The progressive steps of this procedure are as follows:

1. Having tuned in the range, the pilot proceeds to determine which quadrant he is in by flying parallel to the proper quadrant bisectors for a build or fade in signal volume. The detailed steps are identical to those already outlined for other systems initiated with a fade-out procedure.

2. Having determined the quadrant, the pilot arbitrarily

selects which of the two beams bounding it he desires to intersect and adopts a new heading which will be at 90° *to this
beam course.* If, however, the first bisector course had been

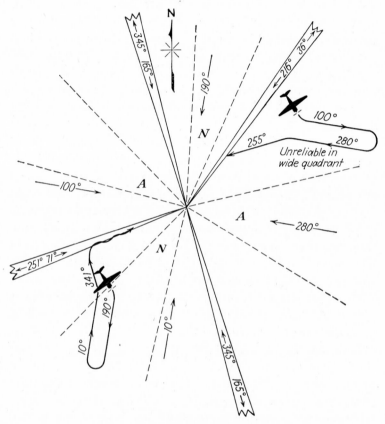

Fig. 21.—Fadeout right-angle system.

away from the station, it is often a better procedure to fly the
reciprocal of this bisector toward the station for approximately the same length of time before adopting the course
toward the beam.

3. Since it is not desirable to intersect a beam at a 90°
angle, the heading should be altered just prior to reaching the

beam. Choose a heading that will provide a closing angle to the beam of about 20 to 30°. Then, when the on-course signal is actually obtained, it will be easier to bracket the beam in the manner explained in Chap. III.

In Fig. 21, the use of this system in two types of range quadrants is illustrated. On the range shown, it will work out well if the orientation has been started in either of the N quadrants. If the orientation had been started in an A quadrant of this range, however, the fade-out right-angle system could very easily lead to further trouble. Note that in the east A quadrant a heading taken at 90° to the southeast beam (255) is just as likely to intersect the northeast beam. *Do not use this system in range quadrants in excess of 90°.*

The Combination System.—In Fig. 22, the so-called "combination system" is diagramed. This again is a special adaptation of one of the three basic orientation systems— the true fade-out—for use on a radio range whose correct beam courses and quadrant bisectors may be unknown. By a comparison of this figure with that illustrating flight paths typifying the true fade-out system, it will be apparent at once that the two procedures differ basically only in the courses used during the original fade-out portion of the problem.

Although it is an unusual situation, it is nevertheless perfectly possible for a pilot to be called upon to orientate on a radio range whose correct beam courses and bisectors are unknown. Possibly he has lost his radio range facility chart or has been furnished with one that is out of date. In actual practice, numerous pilots have been confronted with such a situation when the beam courses of a radio range have been drastically changed by the C.A.A. on short notice.

In actual practice, a pilot would not realize he was confronted with such an orientation problem until he attempted to fly such an altered range with beam courses that no longer existed. To say the least, this is an unexpected situation to which the immediate and normal pilot reaction may very well be momentary confusion. Very likely he has made an

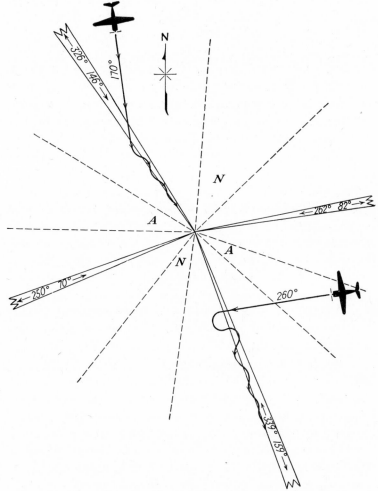

Fig. 22.—Combination system with average of average bisectors.

attempt to bracket a beam on the basis of an erroneous course and soon finds himself lost in an open quadrant. Now, instead of milling around aimlessly or attempting to create imaginary winds of gale force suddenly arising to cause his difficulty, he should adopt the following procedure:

1. If in an N quadrant, arbitrarily select a course of either 170 or 350° and use this as a heading for either a fade-out or build-up in signal volume; if starting from an A quadrant, select a course of either 80 or 260° as the initial heading.

These courses approximate the average of all the average bisector courses for N and A quadrants of ranges within the United States. Note that those for the N quadrants are just 10° less than north and south, whereas those for A quadrants are just 10° less than east and west. These courses, then, may be arbitrarily selected as bisector courses for any range whose correct bisector courses are unknown. Remember in using them, however, that they seldom will represent the correct bisector courses for the particular range being used and thus should not be expected to give identical results.

2. Continue to fly the bisector course selected until *either a definite increase or decrease of signal volume* occurs, or, *lacking this, a change of signal character*. The one (increase or decrease in volume) will indicate whether or not this bisector course is leading toward the station, whereas the latter (change of signal character) will accomplish the same purpose with respect to a beam. Referring again to the figure, it will be evident that by starting as shown with a 170° heading in the north N quadrant, an increase of signal *volume* will inform the pilot that he is approaching the station and should continue on this heading until a beam is intersected. On the other hand, by using a 260° heading from the east A quadrant, it will be the *signal change* from a pure A to a bi-signal A which would be most informative to the pilot.

3. Once a beam has been intersected, it is bracketed with exactly the same procedure as was explained for the true fade-out system. This is often termed an "unknown beam bracket."

CHAPTER V

THE INSTRUMENT APPROACH

Although radio navigation may be used under either contact or instrument flight conditions, it should be evident that the primary purpose of our radio range system and the navigational techniques based upon it is to enable the safe conduct of flight in instrument weather. This means, then, that the radio ranges must not only be used for navigation from point to point, but must also provide a safe means for a pilot to make instrument approaches to desired airports.

At the present development of the art of instrument flying and radio navigation, instrument approach and let-down methods are not designed to allow a pilot to make an actual landing while on instruments. Such a technique is the function of the various blind landing systems now in the process of development. The usual procedure, however, does provide a skillful pilot with a safe means of approaching an airport on instruments while descending to a specified altitude. Such a minimum altitude is seldom less than 300 feet above the field level and is determined individually for each airport. Most of these procedures are designed to place the airplane in a suitable position to make a landing provided that contact flight conditions (hereafter termed "ground contact") exist by the time the minimum altitude is reached. If, however, ground contact is not obtained at minimum altitude, further descent must be abandoned and an alternate airport utilized.

To make possible present-day instrument approach procedures, almost all major airports have a radio range station located near by. In addition, the position of the station is usually such that one of the range courses is directed across the airport or very near to it. Refer to Fig. 23 which illustrates the relation of the Oklahoma City range to the airport.

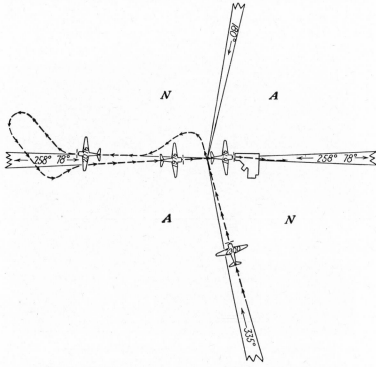

Fig. 23.—Instrument-approach, pattern, Oklahoma City Airport.

BASIC PLAN OF INSTRUMENT-APPROACH PROCEDURE

Although each and every airport must have a specific instrument-approach procedure designed for it, the basic pattern for almost all instrument approaches follows the same general plan. This consists of five parts:

1. Initial approach to the range station.
2. Initial descent on the final approach beam.
3. Final approach to the range station.

4. Descent from the range station to the field.
5. Pull-up if ground contact is not made at minimum altitude.

Referring to Fig. 23, this basic pattern takes the following form when applied to Oklahoma City airport. All altitudes are given above sea level, and all timing is assuming still air.

Under the hood—flight check. (*Courtesy of American Airlines, Inc.*)

For the initial approach to the Oklahoma City range station on any one of the four beams, the pilot maintains 2300 feet above sea level. After passing over the range station, the west beam is used for the final approach. This is first followed away from the station for 3 minutes while descending to 2076 feet above sea level. On this outbound course, the air speed is reduced to the normal approach speed for the particular type of airplane involved (to be discussed later). Simultaneously, the beam heading is ascertained by bracketing, if necessary, in order to determine the drift angle. Likewise, retractable landing gear should be lowered. At the end of 3 minutes, and having reached 2076 feet above sea level, a procedure turn is made to the right so as to return to the station. Returning to the station, the right edge of the beam is followed and further descent made to 1976 feet above sea level by the time the range station is crossed.

The descent from the range station to the field for this approach consists basically of letting down to the minimum of 1676 feet above sea level (this is 400 feet above field level) on the east beam for a sufficient time to reach the edge of the airport. It should be evident that the time from the range station to the airport will depend upon the approach air speed of the airplane being used and the wind conditions prevailing. For example, at Oklahoma City the airport is 1.2 miles from the range station. By using an approach speed of 120 miles per hour, the minimum altitude and the edge of the airport should be reached in approximately 36 seconds in still air.

If ground contact is not established at minimum altitude or at the completion of 1 minute from the range station, the procedure calls for immediate pull-up to 2500 feet on the right side of the east beam.*

It should be evident that the basic pattern of the normal low-approach procedure is designed with several features in mind.

1. The initial approach is maintained at a sufficiently high altitude to clear all obstructions amply between the last radio fix (fan marker, M marker, or beam intersection) and the radio range station. The altitude may be different for the various beams of the radio station.

2. The beam selected for the final approach is usually opposite to that on which the final descent to the field is

---

* Do not use this procedure on Oklahoma City for actual flight. Frequent changes being constantly made in instrument-approach procedures for specific airports necessitate the use of the latest information available.

made. This ensures that the final approach to the range station will also be toward the field; the final descent from the range station to the field can thus be made with little or no change of course.

3. The final approach beam is used to provide the pilot with time and space to descend from his initial approach altitude to the specified final approach altitude at which he should cross the range station a second time. Normally, about one half of this altitude will be lost outbound from the station and the remainder inbound. On the outward course, the pilot is also provided with an opportunity to slow the airplane to the proper approach air speed and let down retractable gear. At the same time, he should bracket the beam to determine the drift angle.

The procedure turn should be made in level flight at the prescribed altitude.

If the pilot has utilized his time outbound on the final approach beam to full advantage, he should be able to concentrate fully during the final approach to the range station on three vital items: establishing his heading on the beam and holding it, maintaining the correct air speed, and descending to the correct altitude for crossing the range station.

If these three items are correct at the moment of crossing the range station the final time, the descent to the field is greatly simplified. First, naturally, the time should be noted upon passing the station. Then, with a straight-in descent, very little change of heading should be necessary to hold the beam; if the final descent necessitates a turn, the amount of turn is easily controlled, provided that the final approach heading has been correctly worked out. Having maintained the correct air speed on the final approach makes the final descent to the field easily and smoothly attained by further reduction in power.

With the final heading and rate of descent established, the pilot is free to concentrate upon altimeter, air speed, and clock. He should plan to reach the minimum altitude prior to the end of his time limit. If ground contact is not made within the specified time, the approach should be abandoned and pull-up made *immediately*.

Specific Instrument-approach Procedures.—The foregoing brief explanation of the instrument-approach pattern at Oklahoma City has been given only to illustrate the reasons underlying the design of all instrument-approach procedures. Almost all of them follow this basic form. Nevertheless, it cannot be too greatly stressed that each airport and range-station combination has its own peculiarities which make necessary a specific instrument-approach procedure for that particular combination. For example, surrounding terrain and other obstructions necessitate very different initial approach altitudes for different airports. Very often initial approach altitudes vary on the same range station, depending upon which beam is used.

Likewise, obstructions may limit the amount of altitude that can be lost on the final approach beam. Also, the permissible minimum altitude over the field, as well as the distance from the range station to the field, vitally influence the final approach altitude over the range station, the final descent, and the time for pull-up.

Still another factor influencing the design of approach procedure is the type of airplane being used. Standard approach procedures designed for airline transports usually have the various time elements computed for approach air speeds varying from 110 to 120 miles per hour (Douglas transports). Naturally, if the airplane being used has a desired approach air speed differing from these figures, the time elements must be altered. One more thing that must be considered in relation to time elements used is the effect of existing wind conditions. All procedures necessarily base their time elements upon still air. This makes it extremely important that a pilot ascertain the probable effect of wind prior to starting his approach and be prepared to alter his timing accordingly.

Faced with all the above-mentioned variable factors which influence instrument-approaches, any pilot should exercise considerable forethought before attempting one. First, it is strongly recommended that none but the most experienced pilots in this type of flying attempt to draw up their own approach procedures. Actually, this seldom should be necessary. It is much safer to obtain the standard airline instrument-approach procedure for the particular airport desired. These procedures are drawn up by airlines for all airports at which their pilots may need them. They are usually printed in map form for each individual airport area and furnish the pilot with necessary information pertaining to that area and the approach to a specific airport. Figures 24 and 25 (see pocket on back cover) show the two sides of such an instrument-approach map as used by a major airline. These airline procedures can be altered by nonairline pilots if need be to conform to the airplane being used as well as the experience of the pilot flying it. Usually, it is only necessary to change the time elements to conform to the desired approach air speed and to raise the minimum altitude over the airport so as to provide less experienced pilots with a greater margin of safety.

SUGGESTED INSTRUMENT-APPROACH TECHNIQUES

It is not the purpose of this chapter to cover the instrument flight technique that must be achieved for a smooth and safe execution of an instrument approach since it is felt that the necessary skill in instrument flying should be achieved prior to attempting radio range flying of any type. Therefore, all suggested techniques to follow will presume the ability to maneuver an airplane skillfully on instruments, and only radio range techniques will be discussed.

Initial Approach.—The initial approach to any radio range station usually does not offer many difficulties. Several factors, however, should be considered. If the direction of approach to the airport area is dependent upon an airway being followed cross country, the beam on which the initial approach must be made to the range station is automatically specified. In this event, the pilot has only to bracket this beam to determine his heading and assume the correct initial approach altitude. He can determine from his radio aid charts how far from the station it is safe to assume this initial approach altitude.

Frequently, however, instrument approaches must be made after the completion of an orientation. This is the case in almost all practice work and in taking C.A.A. rating tests. Such a situation often furnishes the pilot with an opportunity to choose between two beams. Having a choice, he should logically choose the beam that places him in the most advantageous position with respect to the final approach beam. For example, referring to Fig. 23, it should be evident that an initial approach made on the east beam is much more advantageous than one made on any other beam since it eliminates the necessity of turning from one beam to another. Second choice in this instance may be considered the west beam. Then, although the pilot must make a complete turn-around in order to go out the west beam once again for his final approach, he has the advantage of having flown this beam twice before starting his final approach. This gives him an opportunity for a very accurate drift check prior to the final approach.

NOTE.—At this point, it should also be brought out that initial approach altitudes specified for any range station are not necessarily the correct altitudes at which to work out an orientation on this range. In many instances, approach altitudes are only safe to use on or very close to the beams. Since orientations usually necessitate flying in the range quadrants, care must be used to select a sufficiently high altitude while working the orientation to clear *all* obstructions within a wide area of the range station. Such altitudes are often given in the information found on radio range charts.

Turns at the Station.—Very few low-approach procedures specify how a pilot will make the transition from the initial to the final approach beam where a turn must be made. In practice, each approach necessitating such a change of beams is an individual problem. The exact procedure that should be followed in any instance will depend upon several variable factors. Some of these are the amount of turn that must be made to go from the initial to the final approach beam, the accuracy with which the drift has been determined on the initial approach, the wind direction and velocity, and lastly, how promptly the turn is started after passing the station (refer to Fig. 26).

In this figure, the northwest beam is the final approach beam. In position 1 it is assumed that an airplane is making an initial approach on the southwest beam. Unless a strong tail wind has been experienced on the initial approach, good practice would be to make a left turn immediately after passing the range station to a heading that would intersect the northwest beam at an angle of about 30°.

Just prior to making actual contact with the northwest beam, this 30° angle should be reduced in order to expedite subsequent beam bracketing.

Position 2 illustrates the same problem prevailing with an initial approach on the northeast beam. The solution is the same except that the turn is made to the right after passing the range station.

While executing such turns from one beam to another, close attention should be paid to the signal change that takes place. Using position 1 as an example, it will be evident that as a turn is made after passing the range station, a rapid signal transition will take place from an on-course through the bi-signal area to a pure N signal, and then again into the bi-signal zone of the northwest beam. The rapidity with which this transition takes place furnishes the pilot with a good indication of the correctness of his closing angle on the north-

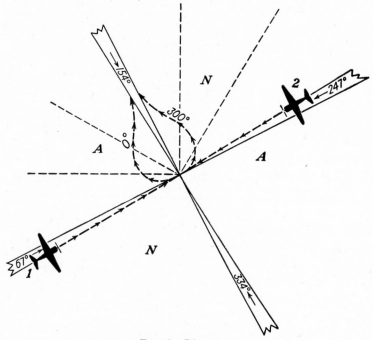

Fig. 26.—Direct turn.

west beam. Skill in signal interpretation during this maneuver allows a pilot to slip into the very narrow on-course of the beam close to the station with a minimum of bracketing.

Figure 27 illustrates an alternate type of turn that may be used to turn from one beam to another. For position 1, it is assumed that a strong tail wind exists on the initial approach beam. If the pilot elected to make a direct left turn toward the final approach beam, the wind effect might seriously delay his reaching the beam. It would be much more advantageous to make a 270° turn to the right after passing the range station so that the wind would carry him toward the beam rather than away from it. This type of turn also provides an accurate time check for the final approach that is not always

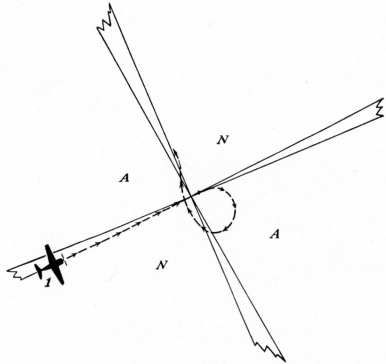

Fig. 27.—Indirect turn.

possible to obtain when a direct turn is made from one beam to another as shown in Fig. 26.

Figure 28 illustrates the preferable course to follow if the initial approach is made on the same beam as is used for the final approach. In this case, instead of making a complete turn-around directly after passing the range station, it is better to continue past the range station for about 2 minutes and make a procedure turn-around on the opposite beam. Although this method consumes slightly more time, it usually ensures a more accurate job of beam flying.

Initial Descent Outbound on the Final Approach Beam.— The outbound course from the range station on the final

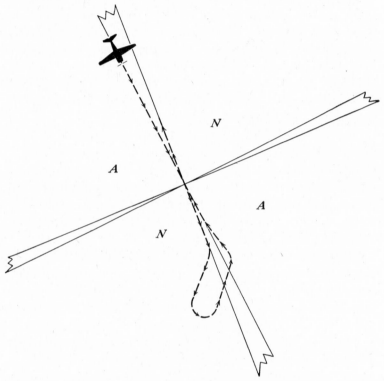

Fig. 28.—Initial approach on final approach beam.

approach beam provides a pilot with the opportunity to do much more than merely lose a portion of his altitude. In many respects, subsequent portions of the approach—final approach and descent to the field—are greatly simplified if the outbound course is used to full advantage.

First, the pilot should not feel that the time factor printed for the approach procedure is ironclad and not to be exceeded (unless so specified due to obstructions). This time factor, if necessary, should be exceeded so that the following items may be properly completed: descent to specified altitude, air speed reduced, the ship trimmed for the desired approach speed, and the drift angle determined. If gear must be lowered, this outward course provides the time to do it.

All these items of maneuvering, losing altitude, and trimming the airplane for the final approach can be accomplished in good shape by a proficient pilot within the time usually allotted. Exceeding this time limit, however, is not a serious error and usually is much better practice than performing an incomplete job prior to the procedure turn.

The procedure turn, itself, should always be made in level flight at the prescribed altitude. In making it, due allowance should be made for the probable drift effect as determined during the initial descent. The subject of procedure turn has been taken up in detail in Chap. III. A proper execution of the turn is essential so that regaining the beam on the final approach is not made a problem.

Final Approach.—Provided that the outbound course on the beam has been smartly flown, the inbound final approach becomes only a matter of attaining the beam, holding it, and once again descending at a normal rate to the final approach altitude. Descent should not be started until the beam is reached after completing the procedure turn. The approach air speed has already been stabilized. Bracketing the beam should not be difficult on the way in if the drift angle already established on the way out can be used to precompute the probable heading. Bracketing procedure, however, should be used as an added precaution and check against any possible change in wind due to the different altitudes. In other words, never assume that a drift angle established at one altitude is necessarily correct for a lower altitude. Beams, especially on the final approach, cannot be flown by dead reckoning.

Final Descent to the Field.—Insofar as the radio range technique is concerned, the final descent to the field is theoretically simple. Given a straight-in approach to the range station from the field, practically no maneuvering should be necessary to hold the beam course if the final approach has been smooth. Sometimes, nevertheless, the beam may be momentarily lost just after passing the range station. In this event, do not succumb to the inviting temptation to make large corrections to regain the beam just because a very broad signal or two is heard. Broad off-course signals should be expected close to the station and do not mean that you are far off the beam. Very likely a turn of a very few degrees promptly made in the right direction will regain the on-course.

Naturally, timing for the final descent over the field should be started directly over the range station. At a low altitude, the cone of silence is very brief and provides an excellent check. Do not forget, however, that the specified time factor may need alteration if appreciable head or tail winds exist.

Descent should not necessarily be at a rate that will attain the minimum altitude at the very moment the approach time elapses. If the surface wind at the airport (and it should be known in advance) is such that a landing can be made directly out of the approach, the rate of descent should be set so as to reach the minimum altitude prior to reaching the edge of the field. If, on the other hand, the surface winds indicate that the airport must be circled prior to landing, it is good procedure to control the descent so that the minimum is reached just prior to the time limit.

The Pull-Up.—The last, but by no means the least, important maneuver incorporated in all instrument-approach procedures is the manner in which the pull-up should be made in the event that ground contact has not been established and the approach is unsuccessful. Usually, the directions for the pull-up are simple. Whenever possible, it is made straight ahead to some specified altitude. In no case should it be delayed past the time limit specified for the final descent from the range station to the field. If ground contact has not been established at the minimum and within the time specified, there is seldom any hope that another few seconds will be of any value. Do not drag across the field at minimum altitude, hoping to pick up a familiar landmark. Remember that ground contact does not mean simply being able to see a spot of ground or a landmark beneath you; but, rather, it means achieving sufficient ceiling and visibility to make a landing by contact flight. Combining instrument and contact flying is a sure road to disaster: there are no experts in this art.

As a final word of advice, too much stress cannot be laid upon each pilot's providing himself with a good margin of safety. Instrument-approach proficiency is not acquired from books or even instruction. An instrument approach, more than any other type of procedure, demands a high degree of proficiency in combining instrument flight technique with radio range flying. Poor technique in either art will probably mean missed approaches: serious errors may mean disaster. The only manner in which to gain proficiency is constant practice. It is for this reason more than any other that airline pilots are masters of this work. To maintain airline schedules, day in and day out, instrument approaches are constantly made. Nevertheless, airline pilots never attempt such approaches at unfamiliar airports and never descend to the authorized minimum at any airports other than those on their regular route. Furthermore, they are *constantly practicing* instrument-approach procedures in airline airplanes and Link Trainers. Even with their high state of efficiency, they know that only constant application will maintain a good margin of safety.

If airline pilots are used as an index, it should be apparent that the average nonairline pilot should exercise great care not to exceed his personal limitations. Frequent practice approaches only can qualify him to attempt a real approach in instrument weather. Likewise, approaches should not be attempted at unfamiliar airports or using unfamiliar procedures. Above all, he should not attempt to use airline minimum altitudes as a standard, but rather raise them to conform to his own proficiency. No pilot can afford to be dishonest with himself in this respect.

CHAPTER VI

THE RADIO DIRECTION-FINDING LOOP

As applied in a practical manner for aircraft, the receiving loop antenna usually consists of several turns of insulated wire wound as a narrow coil. Size varies between 9 and 18 inches in diameter. In addition, the coil is customarily encased within a circular duraluminum tube or a streamlined housing. This not only serves to protect the loop windings but also acts as an electrostatic shield for reduction of precipitation and atmospheric static interference. Actually, a small sector of the tube is cut out, a gap of about one-hundredth of the circumference being left unshielded. This is necessary so that the windings are not completely shielded from the radio waves.

THE AIRCRAFT AURAL-NULL LOOP

Of the many different types of aircraft direction-finding equipment which have been developed around the directional properties of the loop antenna, the most simple and fundamental is the so-called "aural-null direction-finding and anti-static loop." For this reason, and since a clear understanding of aural-null loop operation is necessary for a proper study of other types, subsequent discussion will stress this type of equipment.

As the term implies, the aural-null loop provides the pilot or navigator with aural rather than visual indication of direction. A shielded loop of the type described and capable of being rotated through 360° is used (fixed-position loops are occasionally used but are much more limited in operation than the rotatable type). Within the cockpit is a crank and azimuth scale; the one to provide means of rotating the loop, and the other to indicate its position relative to the airplane's longitudinal axis.

Whenever structural considerations of the airplane permit a choice, preferred mounting of the loop is on the underside of the fuselage near the cockpit. This is particularly true for large metal-covered airplanes, since in this position, the loop receives the incoming waves with a minimum of distortion from the aircraft's structure. This eliminates excessive calibration for deviation errors as well as providing generally better reception characteristics. Mounting the loop well forward near the cockpit shortens the cable length and reduces the possibility of excessive bends between the azimuth crank and the loop and thus eliminates backlash and friction.

Basic Operating Principles of Aural-null Loop.—The directional indication of the aural-null system is based upon the very pronounced variation in signal volume that is heard as the plane of the loop is changed in relation to a transmitting station to which the receiver is tuned. Since the loop is most efficient as an antenna in line with the plane of its windings, the strongest signal is received with the plane of the loop directed toward the transmitter. This position is usually termed the "maximum" or, less commonly, the "anti-static" position. Conversely, since the loop is least efficient in a direction perpendicular to the plane of the windings, either no signal or a signal of minimum volume is heard when the plane of the loop is placed at 90° to the station direction (flat side of the loop toward the transmitter). This is termed the "null position" (refer to Fig. 29).

This diagram illustrates the maximum and null positions of the loop in relation to a transmitter. The position of the null pointers on the azimuth scale within the cockpit is also

shown for each position. In other types of azimuth dials,
two double pointers are used rather than one as shown in this
figure. In that case, the null pointers are usually the longer
pair and are white; the pointers for the maximum are shorter
and colored red. Actually, of course, such an arrangement is
unnecessary as the maximum position is always at 90° to the

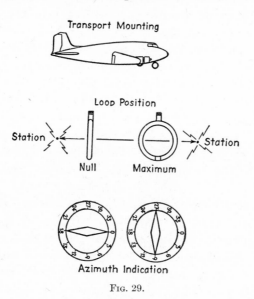

Fig. 29.

null. In still another type of azimuth dial, the scale is
divided into two quadrants of 180° each reading left and right
from the airplane's nose. The left side is marked in red and
the right in green. The only advantage of such a scale is
possible reduction of arithmetic when converting bearings.

It will be noted also that the aural-null loop completely
fails to furnish one very important factor in the determination of direction. That is, whereas the signal response of the
loop will indicate the direction of a line between the loop and
the transmitter, it does not indicate on which side of the loop
the transmitter is located. In other words, only a line of

bearing is furnished, and, until some other means is used to solve the difficulty, it is possible to make a 180° error in the determination of station direction. This is commonly called

Direction-finding loop mounting. (*Courtesy of American Airlines, Inc.*)

"180° ambiguity" and is common to direction finders of the aural-null type. Certain types of direction finders, however, combine a loop with a straight wire antenna in such a manner that this 180° ambiguity is eliminated. In this case, the term "radio compass" is more descriptive than direction finder.

Use of Null.—Although offhand it may appear illogical, all direction finding with the aural-null loop is done with the null position. The desired radio station is tuned in and identified and the loop rotated until the signal either fades out entirely or reaches a minimum. With proper volume setting on the receiver, this null position is considerably sharper and easier to locate than the position of the maximum signal. This is shown by Fig. 30.

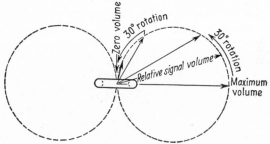

Fɪɢ. 30.—Relative volume change near null and maximum.

Assume that the dotted circles indicate the signal-strength pattern about a loop. The length of any line from the loop center to any point on the dotted circle will represent the signal strength received with the loop at that angle to the transmitter. Obviously, as has been mentioned before, the strongest signal will be received in line with the plane of the loop and, theoretically, a zero signal level at 90° to that position. Moreover, it will be noted that the change of signal intensity is much more rapid as the null position is approached than near the maximum position. This fact makes it possible to establish the null position to within a very few degrees, whereas the maximum may be so broad as to be quite indefinite. In addition to this, the human ear is able to distinguish differences in signal intensity at low levels much more accurately than at high levels.

Use of Maximum.—Although the maximum position is not used for direction finding, it does provide a very valuable means of receiving radio signals through static interference. Two factors contribute to this action. (1) The electrostatic shielding encasing the loop windings tends to minimize the amount of static discharge picked up by the windings. (2) The use of the loop in its most efficient position furnishes a high signal level in relation to the sensitivity level (governed by the volume control of the receiver) carried in the receiver. In other words, using a low volume-control setting and the loop in the maximum position provides a combination of low noise level to high signal level which makes reception through static interference possible.

Null Width and Bearing Accuracy.—Although it should be clear from the foregoing discussion why the null position is used in preference to the maximum for direction finding, it should not be assumed that a null always provides an exact bearing on the transmitter. In this respect, radio bearings by the aural-null method leave something to be desired. A visual bearing taken by a surveyor's transit, for example, can be determined with split-degree accuracy; an aural-null radio bearing taken from an aircraft is difficult to determine closer than two or three degrees. The primary reason is that the human ear is much less efficient in discriminating between minute differences in sound intensity than the eye in distinguishing differences in angular position. Thus the null is practically never an exact point that can be read to the degree on the azimuth scale but rather a zone varying from 2 or 3° in width to as many as 30°. The resultant bearing, then, is necessarily an approximation arrived at by visually splitting the null width on the azimuth scale.

Volume and Null Width.—Of fundamental importance for accurate bearings with the aural-null method is proper control of null width. This is directly dependent upon the strength of the radio signal being received in the headphones.

A high signal volume produces a sharp null, whereas a low volume results in a wide null.

Signal volume in the headphones is the product of several factors. Basically, these are inherent receiver sensitivity plus volume control setting, and transmitter power and distance.

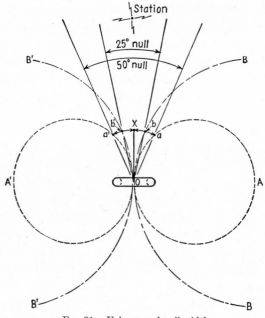

Fig. 31.—Volume and null width.

Receiver sensitivity and transmitter power are constant for any one combination. This leaves distance and the volume control as the variable factors in determining headphone volume and null width.

Figure 31 shows the effects of signal volume in determining null width. The loop null position is directed at the transmitting station. The broken line circles radiating from the loop represent the signal-volume patterns for two different volume levels—AA' representing a low volume and BB' one relatively higher. The straight line OX (drawn of arbitrary length for purposes of illustration) represents the minimum signal volume audible to the average ear.

It will be apparent from the diagram that no signal will be heard until the volume of the received signal is equal to the minimum volume for audibility. With the lower volume pattern AA', the loop must be rotated in either direction until point a or a' coincides with X. With this volume level of received signal, a total loop rotation of 50° is thus allowed during which no signal is audible. This, in effect, becomes a 50° null. By raising the volume level to BB', the signal will become audible with rotation to either b or b' and thus make a null of only 25°. Naturally, these null widths are excessive for actual practice but are used here for the sake of clearer illustration. The point to be emphasized is that under normal conditions the null width is directly controlled by volume. Volume in turn is controlled both by the receiver volume control setting and the distance from the transmitter. Many pilots using the loop in the null position fail to recognize this relationship with resultant difficulties in obtaining a null of proper width and maintaining it as distance to the station is increased or decreased.

Types of Bearing.—As mentioned previously, the position of the loop null is indicated to the pilot or navigator by means of an azimuth scale and pointer which rotates with the loop. Although several variations of azimuth scale design are used, the simplest type is graduated uniformly clockwise from 0 through 360°. All types are mounted in the airplane with the 0 and 180° positions parallel to the longitudinal axis.

This means, then, that all bearings *read directly from such an azimuth scale are only angular measurement in relation to the nose of the airplane.* Such bearings are commonly termed "relative" or "loop" bearings (refer to Fig. 32).

It will be evident that such a relative bearing by itself does not furnish a geographical bearing or direction. For example, in Fig. 32, if the airplane's heading * were unknown, there would be no means of orienting the relative bearing of 30° to north. Thus to reduce a relative bearing to a geographic one, it is necessary to combine it with the airplane's heading as determined from the magnetic compass or direc-

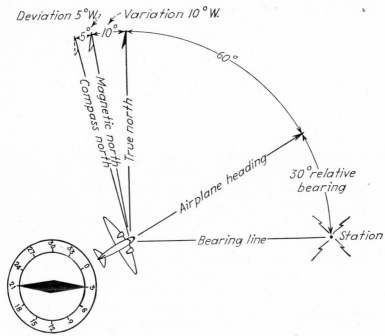

FIG. 32.—Bearings

tional gyro. This relationship is shown graphically in the figure.

Since, however, the airplane's heading may be taken with respect to either true, magnetic, or compass north, we have

* It is important to recognize the exact distinction between the navigational terms "heading" and "course." Heading is the direction toward which the airplane's nose is pointed and obtainable from the compass. Course is the direction in which it is desired that the airplane should travel from one point to another. They differ, of course, because of wind drift.

three similar variations of geographic bearing. These are true bearing, magnetic bearing, and compass bearing. Which will be used is necessarily governed by the particular problem at hand. This will be discussed in a following chapter.

To obtain a geographic bearing mathematically, it is only necessary to add the degrees of relative bearing to the appropriate heading in degrees. From Fig. 32, the following facts can be seen.

1. The *true bearing* equals the true heading, 60°, plus the relative bearing 30°, or 90°.

2. The *magnetic bearing* equals the magnetic heading, 70°, plus the relative bearing 30°, or 100°.

3. The *compass bearing* equals the compass heading, 75°, plus the relative bearing 30°, or 105°.

When the arithmetical sum of heading and relative bearing is more than 360°, it is, of course, necessary to subtract 360 to obtain the resultant geographic bearing. For example, a heading of 300° plus a relative bearing of 80° equals a total of 380°. Subtracting 360 furnishes the correct answer, or a 20° bearing.

Quadrantal Error.—Just as the accuracy of the magnetic compass is adversely influenced by local magnetic fields in the airplane, so are the directional indications of the loop influenced by the metallic structure of the airplane itself. Sometimes, this type of loop error is termed "loop deviation" because of its similarity to compass deviation. Preference, however, is given to the term "quadrantal error" which, although less descriptive, is less likely to cause confusion with compass deviation.

Quadrantal error is caused by the refraction or bending of the incoming radio wave front by the metallic structure of the airplane. This means that the angular position of the loop in relation to the airplane's nose needed to establish a null bearing on the incoming wave will not be an accurate indication of station direction. Unless the amount of this error is known for various positions of the loop and is applied as a correction to the azimuth scale readings, erroneous bearings will result.

The amount of quadrantal error for any loop installation varies as the loop is rotated through the complete 360° of motion. Usually the error will be least at the 0, 90, 180, and 270° points on the azimuth, and greatest midway between these positions. Fortunately, the same pattern of error usually prevails in airplanes of the same type and with similar loop installations.

The quadrantal errors for any specific airplane type and loop mounting are usually determined by one of two methods.

The airplane can be "swung" on the ground in much the same manner as is done to determine compass deviation. A near-by transmitter is selected, and successive bearings are taken at approximately every 30° as the airplane is turned a complete 360°. The difference between the radio bearing as indicated by the loop azimuth and the correct bearing as determined by a pelorus (or other means) is plotted as the quadrantal error. Usually the azimuth scale is adjusted to give zero error on the nose position before swinging is started. Although such a ground check will furnish approximate results, there are usually too many interfering factors present to allow an accurate determination of loop error in this manner.

The preferred procedure for obtaining the values of quadrantal error is to do it in flight. Some prominent landmark is selected at a distance of about 30 to 50 miles from the transmitter to be used. The true direction from this mark to the transmitter is determined from an accurate chart. The airplane is then flown over this mark on prescheduled headings, each time taking a bearing on the station *while directly over the mark*. Usually headings are selected about 30° apart throughout the complete 360°. The difference between the relative bearings obtained and the correct ones computed for each heading becomes the quadrantal error for that particular loop position.

Three common ways of applying the necessary corrections for quadrantal error are in use. In Fig. 33, a typical correc-

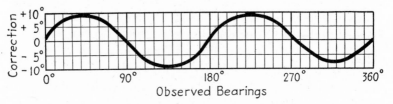

Fig. 33.—Correction curve.

tion curve is illustrated by which the required arithmetical correction to be applied to any observed bearing may be ascertained.

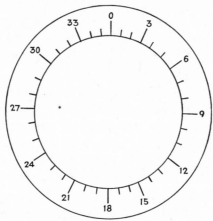

Fig. 34.—Corrected azimuth scale.

In Fig. 34, the corrected azimuth-scale method of applying the corrections is shown. Here the divisions of the scale are so adjusted that the pilot or navigator can read the corrected bearings directly. A third method is to incorporate a specially cut cam between the loop and the azimuth pointer so that the correction is made automatically. This eliminates the need for either correction curve or distorted azimuth scale.

DIRECTION-FINDING INACCURACIES

Night Effect.—In nontechnical terms, "night effect" as applied to the operation of a directional loop consists of shifting (either slowly or rapidly) and indefinite nulls. Sometimes it may be impossible to obtain a null, and then again, there may appear to be several nulls. All loop-type direction finders are subject to these night effects, although the airplane D/F loop is much less affected than a ground direction finder.

Generally speaking, night-effect phenomena are most pronounced during sunrise and sunset periods. Although some degree of this trouble can be expected in hours of total darkness, it is seldom experienced during daylight. Likewise, when it is experienced, it usually disappears when the airplane comes within some minimum distance from the station (varying from 20 to 50 miles).

It is a well-known fact that a conventional transmitter and antenna combination radiates one portion of its energy in the form of a ground wave, which closely parallels the earth's surface, and the remainder as a sky wave, which leaves the surface at an acute angle. The proportion of ground to sky wave is closely related to the frequency of transmission. Low-frequency transmission is predominantly ground wave, whereas the higher the frequency, the more pronounced is the sky wave. In addition, as the frequency increases, the angle at which the sky wave leaves the surface is increased.

This phenomenon of ground and sky wave is of particular importance in direction finding. The behavior of sky-wave radiation is extremely unpredictable since its action is closely governed by the character and height above the earth of the so-called "Heaviside layer" of ionized gases. Acting somewhat in the nature of a fluctuating reflector, it often returns the sky wave to earth out of phase with the ground wave. The net result is night-effect phenomena or sometimes just inaccurate bearings.

Since low-frequency transmission is predominantly by ground wave and thus more accurate for direction finding, most aircraft equipment is designed to operate on low frequencies. In the United States, the radio range (200 to 400 kilocycles) and the commercial broadcast bands (500 to 1500 kilocycles) are preferred.

One of the reasons that ground direction-finding stations have not been used in the United States is that aircraft-communication transmitters are required to operate on intermediate high-frequency bands above 1500 kilocycles. To date, no ground direction finders of sufficient reliability and accuracy have been designed to operate in these frequencies.

Over long distances, however, low-frequency transmission by ground wave requires a prohibitive amount of power. For their transoceanic routes, Pan American Airways have elected to develop their direction-finding network on the basis of aircraft-communication frequencies rather than to construct abnormally high-powered low-frequency stations.

Terrain Effects.—Effects of similar nature to those described are produced by the varying character of the earth's surface itself. The most pronounced errors caused by terrain are bending or refraction of the incoming waves so that a null obtained may be quite an erroneous indication of transmitter direction from the airplane. Bearings taken on stations in mountainous terrain are extremely erratic for this reason. In similar fashion, radio waves traveling over alternate areas of land and water frequently produce erroneous bearings.

Figure 35 illustrates a similar type of effect which may be experienced flying over water and near a coast line. This is commonly termed "coast-line effect." It will be noted that the errors are greatest when the bearings are within 30° of a line parallel to the coast.

All these errors due to terrain will be found to differ considerably with variations in the terrain conditions, and as a

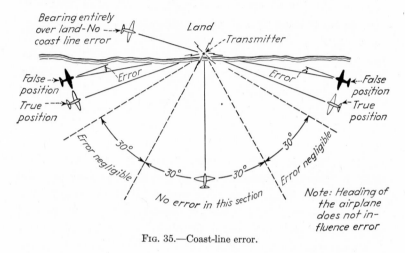

Fig. 35.—Coast-line error.

general rule, they are hard to evaluate. Low altitudes generally make the errors more pronounced and particularly so if high terrain intervenes between the transmitter and the aircraft.

CHAPTER VII

D/F LOOP NAVIGATIONAL TECHNIQUES

If there is any salient advantage in the use of the aircraft direction finder over the several other commonly used methods of navigation it is the essential simplicity of direction-finding technique. This, combined with the navigational flexibility and accuracy which the direction finder affords, should make some form of this equipment a "must" item on any airplane engaged in extended cross-country flight.

Basic Concepts of Direction Finding.—For all explanatory purposes, a radio bearing can be considered as an extension of a visual line of sight. Once this basic idea is clearly recognized, the application of direction-finding techniques to aircraft is readily grasped.

Almost everyone, for example, has observed a surveyor at work. An instrument termed a "transit" is used which consists basically of a telescope and an azimuth scale. The instrument is usually set up so that the 0° of the azimuth scale indicates north. The telescope may be turned through 360°, and the direction of any line of sight may be read in degrees from north on the azimuth.

The relationship of the surveyor's transit to the radio direction finder should be readily apparent. Except that the direction finder's azimuth scale has its 0° point aligned with the airplane's nose instead of north, the scale in each instrument serves the same purpose. It has already been explained how bearings relative to the airplane's nose may be converted to geographical bearings. The null position of the loop takes the place of the telescope and furnishes directional radio bearings instead of visual bearings.

Since this close relationship exists between surveying and radio direction finding, it is not surprising to find that many of the same principles are applicable to each art. Likewise, since the marine navigator's pelorus is nothing more than a special adaptation of the transit for marine navigation, a large portion of aircraft direction-finding technique has been taken from marine practice with the pelorus. This is particularly true in respect to obtaining a fix by means of bearings.

It should not be assumed, however, that the navigational applications of aircraft radio direction finding completely parallel those developed for visual bearings. Recent advanced developments of the automatic and visual indicating radio compass come nearest to accomplishing this. Aural-null direction-finding equipment as distinguished from the radio compass creates certain navigational problems which are completely avoided with either visual or radio compass bearings. (See Chaps. VI and X for the difference between radio compasses and direction finders.)

As commonly used, the aircraft aural-null-type radio direction finder affords the pilot or navigator with an easy means of resolving four basic types of navigational problem. These are as follows:

1. Orientation in relation to a radio station. This consists mainly of solving the 180° ambiguity of bearing common to direction finders. By definition, a radio compass does not have such ambiguity, and therefore the need for orientation problems is eliminated.

2. Homing. This is considered as flight toward a radio transmitter while using a null bearing on that station for continuous directional guidance.

3. Instantaneous position fix. This is a determination of an airplane's geographic position at a specified time by two or more geographic bearings taken in rapid succession (within a period of 2 or 3 minutes) on different radio stations.

4. Running fix. A determination of an airplane's geographic position at a specified time by two or more geographic bearings taken at appreciably different times is termed a running fix. Bearings may be taken on two or more stations and the resultant lines of position adjusted as necessary on the chart to compensate for differences in time, or two bearings separated by a strategic time interval can be taken on one station only and a fix obtained either graphically or trigonometrically.

Principles of Loop Orientation.—Mention has been made in a previous chapter that radio direction finders as distinguished from radio compasses furnish only a *line of bearing* through the position of the airplane and the radio transmitter upon which a null is obtained. In other words, when a null signal is obtained on a transmitter, the general direction of which is uncertain, a choice exists between two bearings exactly 180° apart. The double null pointer on the azimuth scale provides a constant reminder of this.

This characteristic of the direction finder necessitates some orientation procedure to determine which of the two readings on the azimuth scale is the correct bearing on the station.

By a study of Fig. 36, it will be evident that the whole secret of loop orientation is in the relative motion of the airplane and transmitter. Actually, any airplane in flight is always moving forward in relation to a stationary ground transmitter; or expressed differently, the movement of the airplane is always tending to place the transmitter behind the airplane. A little thought will make it evident that this is true regardless of the airplane's course or position with respect to the transmitter. In terms of relative motion, it is easier perhaps to consider the airplane as stationary and the transmitter as continuously moving backward.

Viewed in this manner, then, if a null signal is maintained on a transmitter by rotating the loop while the airplane holds a steady heading, *the null pointer which moves backward from the airplane's nose must point to the transmitter.*

Figure 36 shows this clearly. Two assumed flight paths past a transmitter are indicated: *A* with the station to the right, and *B* with it to the left. A steady heading is being

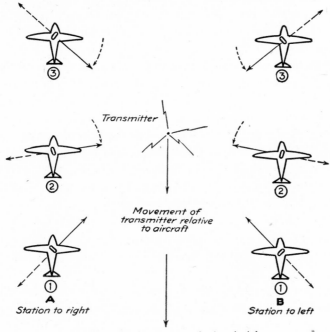

Fig. 36.—Loop orientation—basic principle.

held. The double-pointed arrows represent the typical double null pointer.

In both cases, the indication of the null pointer on the azimuth scale is shown for three positions of the airplane as it moves forward in relation to the station. At position 1, the direction of the station is assumed to be unknown, and thus the null bearing is 180° ambiguous. At positions 2 and 3, the change in null-pointer indication reflects the relative movement of airplane and station. In each case, it will be seen that the null pointer which correctly indicates the station bearing has moved backward from the airplane's nose toward the tail. Therefore the right pointer indicates the station to the right at A, and the left pointer indicates the station to the left at B.

Although it is perfectly possible to resolve the 180° ambiguity of the loop without a more formal procedure than ascertaining the motion of the null pointer, a more positive method is recommended. For example, although the correct relative motion between airplane and station exists, it is impossible to obtain *null-pointer movement* if the station happens to be directly on the nose or tail. Likewise, the angular change in pointer indication will be very slow whenever the original null bearing on the station is near the nose or tail. Since the angular change in pointer indication is most rapid when the null is in line with the wing tips (90° to the longitudinal axis), it is most advantageous to start a loop orientation with a wing-tip null on the station.

LOOP ORIENTATION

Orientation by Pointer-progression Method.—In Fig. 37, a loop-orientation procedure favored by airline pilots is illustrated. It embodies in all respects the principles explained in the foregoing paragraphs.

By assuming that the position of the airplane in relation to the station is unknown, either position 1 or 4 in the diagram is possible with the line of bearing illustrated. To orientate, the following simple procedure is sufficient:

1. Rotate the loop in order to align the null position with the airplane's lateral axis. The null pointer will read 90–270.

2. Execute a standard-rate turn either left or right until a null signal is again picked up. This momentarily places the airplane exactly broadside to the station as in positions 2 and 5. Note the airplane's heading.

3. Continue to fly this heading as accurately as possible,* at the same time rotating the loop as required to hold the null signal.

4. The null pointer that moves backward from the airplane's nose indicates the direction to the station. At posi-

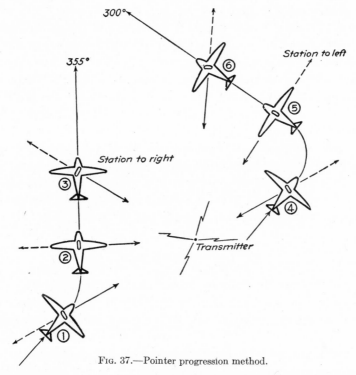

Fig. 37.—Pointer progression method.

tion 3, it is evident that the right pointer indicates the station is to the right; at position 6, the left pointer indicates the station is to the left.

The advantages of this procedure are obvious. It is rapid and positive. It is ideally suited to transport work, for a minimum of airplane maneuvering is required.

* In all subsequent discussion of direction-finding techniques, use of a directional gyro is presumed.

The disadvantages are not quite so apparent. In a small airplane carrying only one pilot, it may be difficult to maintain a steady heading while simultaneously rotating the loop. This is particularly true in rough air or when the loop azimuth crank is inconveniently located. Another theoretical disadvantage is that the distance is increased from the station as the problem is worked.

Although the basic scheme of the orientation procedure outlined above is quite simple, its execution in practice is considerably improved by attention to details of technique. For example, when tuning in the station preparatory to executing the orientation, use the standard antenna for tuning purposes and then switch to the loop. If a loop amplifier is in the circuit, this also must be tuned to the correct frequency before trying to obtain a null.

Though it makes no real difference in which direction the first turn is made in order to pick up the null on the wing tips, it is good practice to choose the direction requiring the least amount of turn. By developing a habit of establishing a null bearing on the desired station before starting *any* turn whatsoever, this problem is simplified. Note which wing tip (90 or 270 on the azimuth scale) is closer to the rearmost null pointer. Make the turn in that direction.

Another suggestion is to make this turn of standard rate (3° per second) in order to minimize the possibility of missing the null signal during the turn. Also, use only a moderate volume while this turn is being made so that the null will be wide enough to guarantee its being recognized. After the turn is stopped, the null width should be reduced to approximately 3°.

The time interval needed to obtain a positive pointer change after attaining the wing-tip null position depends directly upon the airplane's speed and its distance from the station. A minimum of 10° pointer change should be considered reliable. Do not become over-impatient to get results.

Orientation by Heading-progression Method.—An alternative method of loop orientation is illustrated by Fig. 38. Assume that positions 1 and 4 furnish the same problem of orientation as given for the previous procedure. That is, the line of bearing is ambiguous since the general direction

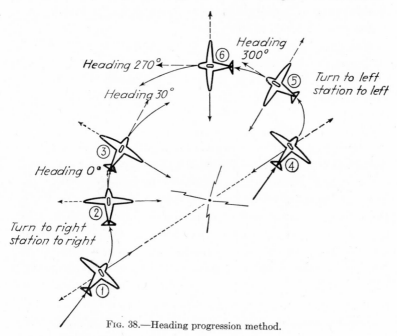

Fig. 38.—Heading progression method.

of the station is unknown. To eliminate this ambiguity, proceed in the following manner:

1. Rotate the loop until the null position is aligned with the airplane's lateral axis. The pointer will read 90–270.

2. Make a turn to either left or right until the null signal is received. This momentarily places the airplane exactly broadside to the station as shown in positions 2 and 5. Note the heading.

3. Adjust the volume control so that the null width is approximately 3°.

4. When the airplane's forward movement has caused loss of the null signal, *immediately* make a *few* degrees of turn to the left or right as required to regain it. It is important that this turn be made the moment the null is lost so that very few degrees of turn need be made to regain it. By acting promptly, it will be readily apparent if a turn is started the wrong way.

5. Continue to hold this null signal by turning the airplane as required, but *do not move the null position from the wing tips*.

6. When sufficient change of the airplane's heading has been noted on the gyro to *positively* determine in which direction it is necessary to turn in order to hold the null signal, the station direction is established.

7. If the turn is made to the right as indicated by the change in heading, the station is to the right as at position 3 in the figure. If a turn has been made to the left, the station is to the left as at position 6.

This procedure is fairly simple to execute in a small airplane or when one pilot is forced to fly the airplane and handle the loop as well. It will be apparent that once the loop-null position has been rotated to the wing tips, no more attention need be given it. The disadvantage of excessive maneuvering makes it less desirable than the previous method for use with a large airplane.

The items of technique, such as station tuning, direction of first turn, and handling of volume control, mentioned in connection with proper execution of the pointer-progression method, likewise apply to this method.

Ascertaining Course to the Station.—At the completion of each of the two loop-orientation procedures just outlined, the general direction of the station from the airplane is established. Although this is the most vital item of information required, a little thought applied to the problem at this point will furnish important supplementary information enabling a pilot to conduct subsequent navigation with intelligence.

A careful pilot will not be satisfied with general direction

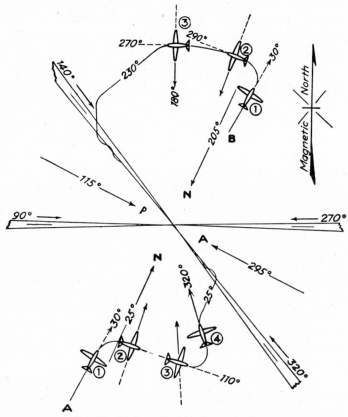

Fig. 39.—Radio-range technique, using loop.

to the station after orientation but will want the *exact* direction. This is very easily obtained.

Referring to Fig. 39, orientation *A* illustrates one method. Simply rotate the loop so that the null position is aligned with the airplane's longitudinal axis and turn toward the station until a null signal is again received as at position 4. The null pointer will read 0–180, and as long as the null is being received in this position, the airplane is pointed directly at the station. The directional gyro will indicate the magnetic *course* to the station *at that instant*—in this example 340°. Note that *course* and *not heading* is obtained. It is necessary to compensate for the effect of wind drift in order to obtain the heading to fly to make good this course. This will be discussed under Homing.

Another method is to obtain the course to the station after orientation by computation. At the moment of establishing the general direction of the station from the airplane, note the gyro heading. Then simply add or subtract as required the angle that the appropriate null pointer indicates from the airplane's nose. Add if the station is to the right, and subtract if to the left. For example, as shown in Fig. 39, orientation *A*, the direction to the station is known at position 3. The gyro heading at that instant is 110°. The left null pointer is 115° off the nose. The result is a course of 355° to the station from position 3.

Such arithmetic is apt to be confusing under the pressure of instrument flying and orientation when odd figures must be handled as in the preceding example. Therefore, after a pointer-progression type of orientation, it is suggested that the course to the station be found by obtaining a nose null on the station.

Referring to Fig. 39, orientation *B*, it will be evident that computation is extremely easy when used with a heading-progression type of orientation. A distinctive feature of the system is that the loop-null position remains constantly at 90° to the heading. Therefore, as the orientation is completed, note the heading and add or subtract 90° as required to compute the exact course to the station. As illustrated at position 3, this course is 270 − 90, or 180°. This avoids both turning the airplane and rotating the loop.

Ascertaining the course from the airplane's position to a station is essential information regardless of what is done thereafter. When orientating on a nondirectional transmitter such as a broadcast station, this information furnishes the exact direction of the station and may be flown as a course to the station. A radio range station, however, offers considerable choice as to subsequent plan of action. For in this case, orientation not only provides the general direction to the station but automatically establishes in which quadrant the airplane is located. Referring again to Fig. 39, this fact is easily visualized. If the quadrant is known, it is usually better practice to proceed to the nearest radio beam than to fly directly to the station proper. The reasons for this will become more apparent in discussing homing procedures.

Selecting Nearer Beam.—Picking the nearer beam and proceeding to it is a very simple technique. Referring to Fig. 39, orientation *B*, it will be seen that the exact bearing to the station at the completion of the orientation (position 3) has been established as 180°. Determine by inspection between which beam course and quadrant bisector this figure lies. In the situation illustrated, it lies between the 140° beam course and the 205° bisector. Thus, the 140° beam is the nearer. Thereafter, assume a heading to converge upon this beam at 90° and change over to the standard range antenna. From this point on, the problem is strictly radio range flying.

In Fig. 39, orientation *A*, the same procedure is illustrated with slight variations, the course of 340° to the station having been established at position 4 as previously explained. The 320° beam is selected. Since a 340° course is only 20° different from the beam course, the airplane's position is shown to be very close to the beam. In such a position, the quadrant bisector of 25° provides a sufficient angle of convergence to be used as a heading to the beam.

HOMING

Homing is the term applied to the technique of flying toward a radio transmitter by use of the null signal for directional guidance.

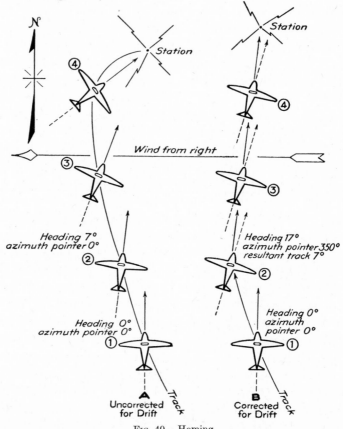

Fig. 40.—Homing.

The simplest method is to set the null position in line with the airplane's longitudinal axis (null pointer 0–180) and turn the airplane until a null signal is received. Maintain this null signal by adjusting the airplane's heading as required. Though this will keep the nose at all times directed at the station, it provides no allowance for possible wind drift. Thus, a curved track is usually made good as shown by Fig. 40, diagram *A*. Such a curve theoretically places the airplane directly into the wind at the moment of crossing the station.

The chief disadvantage of homing without drift correction is the curved track rather than the time lost (this may be negligible). To compensate for drift and thus achieve a straight track is very simple. Start homing as directed above with the loop-null position on the nose, and note the heading. Hold the heading, and as the null signal is lost, rotate the loop either left or right to regain it. If the drift is toward the *left*, the new loop-null position will be to the *right* of the nose. Assuming that it becomes 10° to the right, turn the airplane slightly more than 10° right (into the wind), reset the null position approximately 10° to the left of the nose (downwind), and fly the null signal. Refer to Fig. 40, diagram *B*, positions 1 and 2. After one or two trials, it will soon be possible to find a loop-null setting and a heading that will *remain constant*. Drift has then been compensated, and a straight track will be flown to the station. In setting the loop-null position, the following simple rule is helpful: always set the null pointer to the *downwind side* of the airplane's nose.

Determination of Station.—In practical navigation when homing on a radio range station, there is very little advantage in holding a homing course directly to the range station. If on instruments and an approach must be executed, the best plan is to abandon homing when the rate of signal build-up indicates that the station is not far distant and proceed to the nearest range beam. Since the actual instrument approach must be made with the use of range beams and conventional nondirective antenna, it is better practice to change over before arriving at the station rather than after reaching it.

Nevertheless, it may be necessary under emergency conditions to continue homing directly to a station. The chief difficulty in this is to determine the exact moment of passing over the station.

In airline aircraft, a pilot is assisted in identifying station passage in one or two ways not usually available to the itinerant pilot. He may use the Z marker on ranges so equipped or request his co-pilot to check the cone of silence on a second receiver. Under emergency conditions with expert use of the loop, station passage can usually be determined in the following manner.*

While inbound on the homing course, maintain a null width of approximately 5°. As the station is approached, a more frequent rate of volume-control adjustment will be needed to do this. At the same time, this indicates the increasing proximity of the station. Check the null width with increasing frequency as you near the station, either by kicking the rudder slightly or by rotating the loop. Simultaneously, of course, the build-up of signal volume will be noticed.

Just prior to the station, the tendency is for the null width to decrease and the signal strength to increase very rapidly. Hold the null width at 5° if possible until at the very moment of crossing the station; a distinct *surge* will replace the null completely. With the *loop in homing position*, this surge corresponds to the conventional cone of silence. After the station is passed, the null will reappear. Figure 41, diagram *B*, shows this graphically, whereas diagram *C* shows the ideal change in volume-control setting for the same procedure.

It will be evident from the foregoing discussion that in addition to proper technique with the volume control it is necessary to have sufficient time interval over the station *to be certain* the null has been replaced by the surge rather than

---

* Loop installation on the airplane is an important factor affecting the success of the above procedure.

simply lost while checking it. Sufficient altitude over the station is the only answer. Figure 41, diagram *A*, indicates the minimum altitude that should be used for the speed ranges plotted.

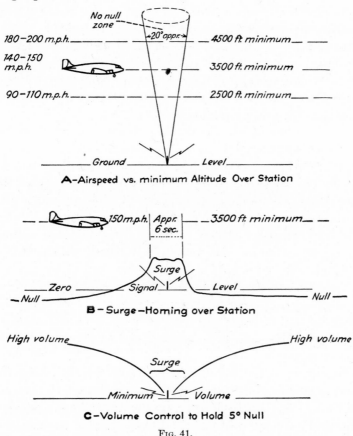

A—Airspeed vs. minimum Altitude Over Station

B—Surge—Homing over Station

C—Volume Control to Hold 5° Null

Fig. 41.

Although the method of station passage identification just explained will usually be successful when skillfully performed, there will be times when a pilot may not establish the station with sufficient certainty to justify its acceptance. An additional check is to reset the loop-null position at 90–270 on the azimuth scale and recheck the station location by an orientation procedure. Since the position should be very close to the station, this check may be performed very quickly.

An alternative method for proving station passage is to fly slightly to one side of the station and follow the rapidly changing null by rotating the loop. The difficulty with this method is choosing the proper moment to abandon the homing procedure and adopt a heading that will pass the station to the side. For best results, this should be done at the very last moment prior to reaching the station.

CHAPTER VIII

POSITION FIXES BY D/F BEARINGS

Stated simply, a position fix as applied to aircraft consists of determining the position on the earth's surface above which the aircraft is flying at a specified time. Determination of such a fix, of course, may be accomplished by any one of several means other than radio bearings, such as by visual reference to ground objects, radio markers, intersections of radio beams, or celestial lines of position. Likewise, definition of the position may be made by any one of several means of reference, such as over a prominent landmark, by direction and distance from any easily specified place on the earth's surface, a recognized radio beam intersection, or latitude and longitude. By whatever means determined or defined, however, any fix denotes a definite geographic spot readily located on a suitable chart representing the earth's surface.

It will be apparent, then, that the fundamental prerequisite for obtaining a fix by radio (or other means) is sufficient information to locate the airplane in relation to the earth's surface. With standard receiving equipment (nondirective antenna) for radio range flying, this means that a radio fix is possible only at the intersection of two beams or over a cone of silence or low-frequency M type marker. An ultra-high-frequency marker receiver, of course, increases the fix possibilities by enabling use of the great number of fan and approach markers now in operation. Even so, it should be readily apparent that the inflexibility of the radio range system severely limits the availability of radio position fixes when only a nondirective receiving antenna is used.

The rotatable direction-finding loop provides the ideal means of obtaining a radio fix. Though its accuracy in this respect is not so good when mounted in an airplane as when on the ground, the flexibility of the aircraft loop, plus the fact that it is available for other purposes, outweighs this drawback. With the direction finder, a pilot or navigator can at any time and from any position obtain a directional bearing on any radio transmitter that the receiver will pick up. Thus by a proper use of such bearings on one or more stations, the possibility of obtaining a fix is always present.

The direction finder offers two general methods for obtaining a fix. The first, for want of a better name, is termed an "instantaneous fix." By this method, bearings are taken on two or more radio stations as rapidly as possible. These are then converted from relative to geographic bearings for plotting on the chart. The intersection of two or more lines of bearing denotes the position.

The second general method of obtaining a fix with the direction finder is termed a "running fix." In practice, this is done by taking two or more bearings on either one or two stations with an appreciable time interval elapsing between bearings. If only one station is used, the angular change of bearing which takes place as the airplane moves in relation to the station is combined with the distance the airplane moves between the bearings. By solving some type of plane triangle from this known information, the distance and direction of the airplane from the station can be calculated. When two stations are used, the first bearing taken is advanced in proportion to the airplane's movement between the time of the first and second bearings. This, in effect, simply advances the first line of bearing so that it is plotted as if taken at the same time as the second bearing.

THE INSTANTANEOUS FIX

Basic Requirements.—As previously stated, the prerequisite to obtain a fix is sufficient information to locate the airplane with respect to the earth's surface at a definite time.

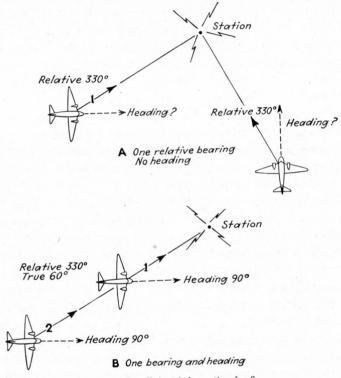

Fig. 42.—Insufficient information for fix.

Such a conception means, then, that any bearing taken with the aircraft direction finder must in some manner be converted from a relative to a geographic bearing (either true or magnetic). This is necessary so that the line of bearing can be plotted on the chart. This is shown by Fig. 42*A* which illustrates how a relative bearing alone fails to establish a line of bearing to the station. In Fig. 42*B* is shown this relative bearing converted to a true bearing by combining it with the airplane's true heading. In this case, the airplane is placed on a line of bearing of 60° toward the station. It will be apparent, however, that insufficient information is available to fix the airplane's distance from the station.

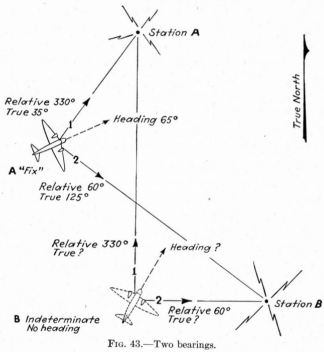

Fig. 43.—Two bearings.

In Fig. 43*A*, the minimum requirements for a position fix are illustrated. These are two geographic bearings. As usually obtained in practice, this amounts to taking in rapid succession two relative bearings which, when combined with the airplane's heading, automatically become two geographic bearings. Figure 43*B* is shown to emphasize why the airplane's heading must be known. Since the bearings as read from the azimuth dial are always relative bearings, the airplane's heading must be known to orientate these geographically on a chart.

Restated in other terms, two intersecting lines of geographical bearing on separate radio stations are the minimum requirements for an instantaneous fix. In practice, this minimum requirement is satisfied by two relative bearings plus the airplane's heading. The mean time between the moments of obtaining the first and second bearing is used as the time of the fix.

Since it is essential that the airplane's heading be known to enable conversion of relative bearings as read from the loop azimuth scale into geographic bearings, it should be emphasized that an accurate magnetic compass becomes as much a requirement for a radio fix as the direction finder itself.

One exception does exist, however, by which it is possible to obtain a fix when the heading is unknown. Such a condition might arise in practice, if for one reason or another the magnetic compass has failed. Then three relative bearings taken in rapid succession on three different radio stations will usually provide a fix. The plotting of such a fix becomes much simpler with a three-arm protractor of the type shown in Fig. 44 than by other plotting systems. This will be discussed in detail in a later paragraph.

Practical Combinations.—As previously stated, the minimum requirements for an instantaneous position fix are two intersecting lines of geographic bearing taken as near simultaneously as possible on separate radio stations.

This condition may be met as previously illustrated by Fig. 43*A*. Two relative bearings will be taken in rapid succession on different radio stations. Combined with a known heading, which has been flown steadily during the shots, and the mean time, sufficient information is given to plot the fix.

Figure 45 illustrates a variation of this procedure which is very useful when flying a radio range beam. Although it is necessary to take only one bearing with the direction finder,

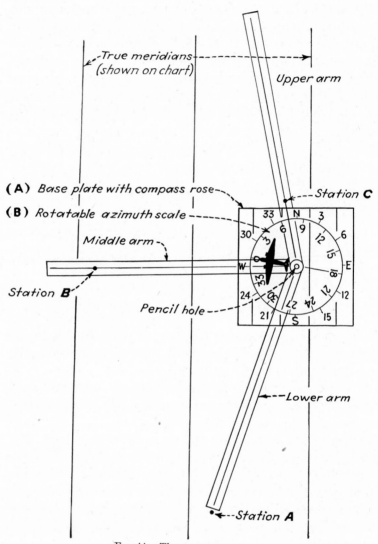

FIG. 44.—Three-arm protractor.

it will be seen that the known beam course effectually fulfills the function of a second bearing. In airline practice, this method of getting a fix with the direction finder is frequently used. Being very rapid and simple to perform, a fix obtained in this manner usually is accurate. It will be apparent that a pilot can use this system to check his position at any time while flying a beam. In fact, by precomputing what the side bearing should be at some selected point (or time) along the

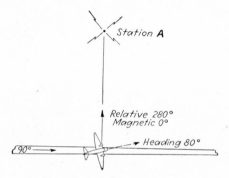

Fig. 45.—One bearing and beam.

beam, it is easy to preset the loop to the correct azimuth reading. When the null is received, the airplane is over the selected point.

For example, in Fig. 45 assume that the pilot wishes to ascertain the moment of passage over a point due south of station *A*. Having established that a heading of 80° magnetic is needed to hold the 90° magnetic beam course, it is seen that the null pointer must be set to 280–100 on the azimuth scale to obtain a magnetic bearing of 0° to the station. At the moment the null is received, the airplane must be due south of the station. In this instance, magnetic rather than true bearings are used, since beam courses are customarily published in degrees magnetic.

Although two bearings and a heading represent the minimum requirements for a fix, three bearings and a heading usually provide a more positive position. In this case, the third bearing may be considered in the light of an added check. As will be shown when plotting is discussed, the third bearing often discloses inaccuracies in the shots and provides a means of evaluating the accuracy of the plotted position.

Taking three rather than only two bearings will often disclose possible errors introduced when converting the relative bearings to true or magnetic bearings. Occasionally such errors are caused by a faulty compass rather than erroneous bearings. By having three relative bearings, then, it is still possible to plot the position without using the heading.

Preparation Prior to Taking Bearings.—Probably the most common mistake made when taking bearings in flight is starting to take the bearings without devoting sufficient advance thought to the problem. Invariably, the amateur at the job will just decide to take bearings and, with no further preparation, start in. Inevitably, the result is confusion, wasted time, and a fix of dubious accuracy.

The accuracy of any position fix by means of radio bearings is almost equally dependent upon the skill with which the bearings are taken and the skill with which they are translated into a fix by plotting on the map. For the moment, discussion will be limited to actually taking the bearings.

Several factors enter into this operation to influence the resultant usefulness of the bearings in plotting the fix. These should be considered prior to actually taking the bearings and the plan of operation formulated mentally so that the actual operation of using the direction finder may be performed as rapidly as possible.

First, it should be realized that a fix is dependent upon the intersection of two or more lines of bearing on different radio stations. With this in mind, it should be apparent that the two lines of bearing should not intersect at relatively small angles since a minor inaccuracy in one of the two bearings will result in a major displacement of the intersection. Usually, it is not considered wise to take bearings on stations that will produce less than a 30° or greater than a 150° angle between the intersecting lines of bearing. In addition, when only two bearings are used, the angle between one line of position and the meridian should be not less than 30° or greater than 150°. This is shown diagrammatically in Fig. 46.

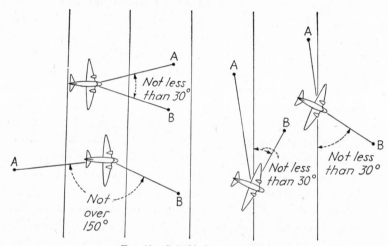

Fig. 46.—Suitable bearing angles.

Although the selection of stations giving desirable angles of intersection to the lines of bearing is an important consideration, other factors also exist to influence the selection. The more distant the station, the wider the null is likely to be, and therefore, the greater possibility of bearing error exists. When possible, select high-powered stations within 150 miles which promise a relatively good null in preference to low-powered or distant stations. On the other hand, stations at less than 25 miles distance are not always favorable owing to the rapid angular change in bearing caused by the airplane's movement. This latter effect is minimized, of course, if the station bearing lies within a few degrees of the nose or tail of the airplane.

Having mentally selected the desired stations, it is often wise to tune each of them in on the regular receiving antenna as a check prior to taking bearings. It is a good plan at this point to write down the identification letters and frequency of each station to be used. Whereas some type of printed D/F log sheet is unquestionably a help if position fixes by bearings are a regular routine, it is probable that the average pilot will not be so provided (refer to Fig. 47). In this event, he should not trust too much to his memory but should note down all

Radio D/F Bearing Log							
Date_____ Trip _____ Crew _____ Nc_____							
D.R.Position	Heading	No.1 Bearing and Time	No.2 Bearing	No.3 Bearing and Time	Time of Fix	Plotted Position	Remarks

necessary information for quick reference and, especially when taking the bearings, should not fail to write each down as taken.

The final item to decide is the order in which the bearings will be taken. Unless otherwise desirable, the most rapid procedure is to take the bearings in order of the station frequency. This eliminates unnecessary cranking of the tuning controls. Sometimes, however, when a station is both fairly close and broadside to the airplane's direction of motion, it is best to take this bearing as the second of three bearings so that it will coincide approximately with the mean time of the three.

From the time taken to outline these factors which must be considered before taking the bearings, it might appear that it is necessary to deliberate at great length each time it is desired to take a fix. In practice, just the reverse is true. Usually, if the approximate position of the airplane is known from dead reckoning, a very brief inspection of the map will immediately suggest desirable stations to use. Checking their reception prior to actually using the direction finder is not always necessary; yet, whenever any doubt exists that the desired stations may be picked up, it is a sensible precaution. In other words, what is being recommended is that everything possible be done prior to actually taking bearings to ensure that they will be *accurate* and *useful*. The more of these items that can be decided upon ahead of time, the less time will be needed with the direction finder. This is an important consideration, since the longer the time needed to take bearings, the greater will be the error in the fix caused by the airplane's movement.

Technique with Direction Finder.—Provided that proper thought has been given to the problem beforehand, the actual operation of taking sufficient bearings for a fix is a relatively simple matter. The two most important points in taking the bearings are to obtain as accurate a null as possible on each station and to complete the whole operation without waste of time. With practice, it should be possible to obtain bearings on three different stations within a total elapsed time of 2 minutes. Since the operation of taking three bearings on three different stations may be considered the most difficult case met in practice, a suggested technique for accomplishing this rapidly is as follows:

1. Note and write down the magnetic heading of the airplane. Hold this as accurately as possible while taking the bearings.

2. Tune in the station on which the first bearing is to be taken. This may be done by using standard antenna, or, if the approximate direction to the station is known, on the loop. If the station is tuned in on the loop, care must be exercised that the maximum position of the loop is pointed in the general direction of the station so that the signal will be heard. Make station identification positive by waiting for the identification signals.

3. Using as high a volume level as practical, obtain a null bearing on the station. Write this down and the time of obtaining it.

4. Tune in the second station as was done for the first. Make identification positive, and obtain the null. Write the bearing down. (The time does not need to be taken.)

5. Repeat as above for third station, and note the time the third bearing was obtained.

6. Using the time of the first and third bearings, mentally calculate the mean time. This will be used as the time of the fix.

In actual practice, it is not always easy to decide exactly where the null comes on the azimuth dial. As explained in a previous chapter, the higher the signal level, the narrower will this zone of null be. Nevertheless, it is seldom a definite point. To obtain a dial reading that will be used as the bearing, the loop should be slowly rotated through the null zone and the two readings at which the signal becomes audible noted. Taking the mid-point between these usually gives an accurate bearing. This is often termed "splitting a null."

Frequently, the atmospheric noise level prohibits the use of a high volume. If so, a wide null may be split in the manner just explained. It will be accurate as long as the two readings defining the width of the null are carefully obtained.

A common fault often observed with beginners in taking bearings is that too much time is wasted in trying to decide the exact location of the null. Although precision is an asset, probably it will not be gained by indecisive rotation back and forth through the null. One or two trials at most should be sufficient.

Any bearings taken that are considered of doubtful value should be noted as such. Although a pilot in flight can remember this if he is plotting it himself, it is necessary that the man on the ground be definitely advised of doubtful bearings if the position is to be plotted by ground personnel.

PLOTTING TECHNIQUES

As previously explained, a position fix by *D/F* bearings is
determined by the intersection of two or more radio lines of

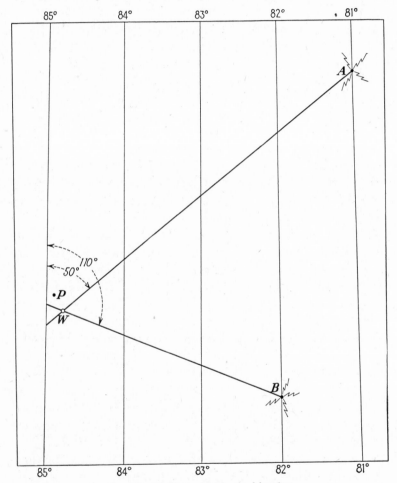

Fig. 48.—Plotting with observed bearing.

bearing. Since a fix represents a definite geographical position over the earth's surface, it is always determined by

some method of graphical plotting on a chart representing the proper area of the earth.

All methods of plotting are directed toward the same goal, *i.e.*, finding the spot where the given lines of bearing intersect.

Plotting from an Assumed Position.—One very simple system of plotting bearings is to convert each relative bearing as read from the azimuth scale to a true bearing and draw each as a line of position on any suitable chart (refer to Fig. 48).

A pilot flying in the vicinity of point P determines the relative bearing of station A as 325° and the relative bearing of station B as 25°. The magnetic heading at the time is 90°, variation is 5° west.

First, the true heading is found to be 85° (90 − 5). The true bearing on station A is 50° (85 + 325 − 360), and on station B it is 110° (85 + 25).

He is uncertain of his position but assumes that he is near the point P. The true bearing of station A is plotted on the chart, the meridian nearest the assumed position being used and the protractor being moved along that meridian until the line of bearing passes through the radio station. In similar fashion, the line of bearing to station B is plotted. The intersection of the two lines of bearing gives the fix at W.

It will be noted that the procedure explained above plots the various lines of bearing from the meridian nearest the airplane's assumed position to the radio stations. In effect, this is plotting from the airplane toward the station. Since it requires no computation other than converting the original relative bearings to true bearings, this method is very simple.

Plotting at the Radio Stations.—An alternate procedure is to plot the respective lines of bearing as if the bearings had been taken on the airplane from the radio stations. This consists of plotting at the radio stations toward the airplane. In a like manner, of course, the intersection of two or more such lines of bearing will establish the fix.

To plot in this manner, the original relative bearings taken at the airplane are converted to true bearings as before.

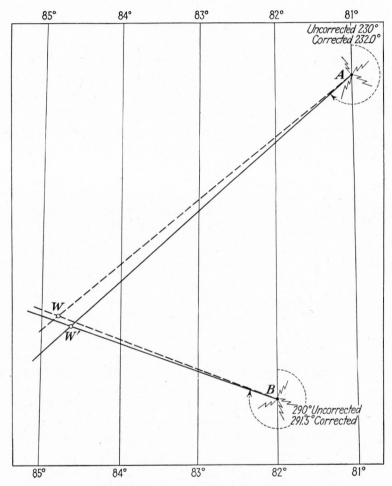

FIG. 49.—Plotting with reciprocal bearings.

These true bearings are then further converted into their reciprocals (add or subtract 180°) (refer to Fig. 49).

By using the same bearings as in the previous problem, the

solid lines illustrate the plotting of this fix in the manner just described. The true bearing of 50° on station *A* has been converted to its reciprocal of 230°. A line of bearing representing 230° has then been laid out from station *A*. In like manner, the true bearing of 110° from the airplane to station *B* has been converted to its reciprocal of 290°. A line of bearing representing 290° has then been laid out from station *B*. The point of intersection *W'* represents the fix.

Allowance for Meridian Convergence.—Although a bearing taken from the airplane may be plotted from the station after a simple conversion to its reciprocal, actually the procedure is not accurate when using most aeronautical charts.

A radio bearing over the earth's surface follows an arc of a great circle which is the shortest distance between any two points on the surface of a sphere. Such an arc, however, does not intersect the north and south meridian lines on the sphere at a constant angle (except at the equator). This is due to the fact that the meridians are not parallel but have a definite angle of convergence toward one another as they approach the poles.

For aeronautical navigation within the United States, almost all charts are based upon the Lambert Conformal Conic projection. Among other salient advantages that charts based upon this projection possess is the very important fact that any arc of a great circle across the earth is represented on the chart as a *straight line*. To make this possible, then, the meridians on the chart must show a definite angle of convergence toward the poles.

Therefore, although lines of bearing may be drawn on such charts as straight lines, they actually cross each meridian line at a slightly different angle.

In other words, a line of bearing between an airplane and a radio station located on different meridians will cross successive meridians on the chart at a constantly changing angle throughout its length. Thus it follows that a bearing taken on a station from an airplane will not be represented correctly by merely plotting its reciprocal from the station toward the airplane. By a careful check of Fig. 48 with an accurate protractor, it will be evident that the bearing of the airplane from station A is not 230° (the exact reciprocal of 50°) but is closer to 232½°. This discrepancy is due to meridian convergence.

To plot bearings correctly from the station, it is necessary to take meridian convergence into account. When using United States charts based upon the Lambert Conformal projection, this convergence angle between any two meridians is approximately 0.6°.* This amount must be applied as a correction factor to the reciprocal bearing for each degree of longitude separating the airplane from the station.

If the airplane is to the east of the station, the rule is to subtract 0.6° from the bearing of each degree of longitude separating airplane and station; if the airplane is to the west of the station, add 0.6° to the computed reciprocal bearing for each degree of longitude separating airplane and station.

It will be evident that this correction may, for all practical purposes, be neglected when the station and airplane are not more than 2° of longitude apart. Bearings taken over longer distances, however, should be corrected if accuracy is desired.

Figure 49 also shows the correct plotting of the fix used as an example after the reciprocals of the original bearings have been corrected for meridian convergence. Approximately 2° have been added to the reciprocal bearing at station A and approximately 1½° to station B. These corrected bearings have been drawn as broken lines. Their intersection at W represents the true fix. Note that the true fix W is in agreement in both Figs. 48 and 49, whereas W' in Fig. 49 is slightly in error.

* A correction factor of 0.6° is sufficiently accurate to use for Lambert charts between 30 and 45° latitude. South of 30° latitude, the correction factor should be decreased until it becomes zero at the equator. Above 45° latitude, the correction factor increases until it is 1° at the poles.

Special D/F Charts.—A variation of this method of plotting with reciprocal bearings makes use of special radio direction-finding charts printed by the U. S. Coast and Geodetic Survey office. These, like the sectional and regional

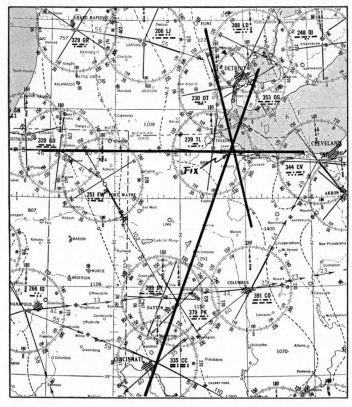

Fig. 50.

aeronautical charts, are constructed on the Lambert projection at a scale of one to two million (see Fig. 50).

Around each radio range station is printed a special compass rose oriented to magnetic north instead of true north. These compass roses are designed primarily to facilitate plotting the lines of bearing *from the station* rather than at the meridian nearest the assumed position. On these D/F maps, the outer figures of the compass rose provide this conversion to reciprocals directly and thus save time and eliminate errors in arithmetic. The following example will illustrate the use of these charts:

The pilot takes three relative bearings as follows: Cincinnati, 280°; Goshen, 350°; and Detroit, 70°. The magnetic heading is 280°; variation at the airplane's approximate location is considered as 3° west.

Since the compass roses on the map represent magnetic directions, the relative bearings need be converted only to magnetic rather than true bearings. These are Cincinnati, 200° (280 + 280 − 360); Goshen, 270° (280 + 350 − 360); and Detroit, 350° (280 + 70).

To plot, refer to Fig. 50. Using the above magnetic bearings and the outer numbers on the compass rose at each station, construct three lines of bearing as shown. These three lines of bearing do not intersect at one common point but form a small triangle. This is due to the movement of the airplane while the bearings are being taken. If this triangle appears overly large, the most probable position of the airplane is at the center of the triangle.

This method of plotting on the special D/F chart can be considered the most practical of those explained so far. The only conversion necessary in most problems is from relative to magnetic bearings. Since the compass roses are oriented to magnetic rather than to true north and are likewise designed to eliminate arithmetical computations of reciprocals, the whole problem of plotting becomes relatively simple.

The use of these special D/F charts, of course, does not eliminate the necessity of applying corrections for meridian convergence when utmost accuracy is required. When this is done, the same rules previously quoted are applicable.

Although the orientation of the compass roses eliminates the need for converting the bearings to true, this scheme

automatically introduces an additional correction. When
the magnetic variation in the area of the station differs from
that in which the airplane is located, the amount by which
they differ must be applied as a correction to the reciprocal
bearing. This is applied in the following manner.

The difference between the magnetic variation at the airplane and at the radio station should be *added* if the variation
at the airplane is smaller in west variation areas; subtract
under reverse conditions. Generally, this correction will be
applied in the same manner as the correction for convergence.

THREE-ARM PROTRACTOR POSITION PLOTTING

The chief fault of the two methods of plotting positions
which have just been described is that they are difficult to
perform in the cockpit of the average airplane. For plotting
positions in the cockpit, a special three-arm protractor of the
type shown by Fig. 44 is recommended. American Airlines
has developed this for use in conjunction with a special direction-finding strip map. The mileage scales stamped on the
arms of the protractor match the scale of the charts (1 inch
= 24 miles). A separate chart is made up to cover each section of the country flown by this company. Also to facilitate
use in the cockpit, the charts are mounted on a special plotting board which allows the portions of the map not being
used to be rolled out of the way.

Use of Three-arm Protractor.—The use of the three-arm
protractor is extremely simple. In Fig. 44, this instrument is
shown as set to duplicate the plotting of the same fix shown
in Fig. 50. To set up any problem on this protractor, it is
only necessary to realize that the base plate A, when properly oriented on the chart, represents a compass rose. The
rotatable azimuth scale B, with the sketch of the little airplane, corresponds to the airplane's loop azimuth scale, and
each arm can be set to represent one bearing. On the rotatable

scale, it will read as a relative bearing; on the base plate *A*, it will read as a true bearing, provided that the zero of scale *B* (corresponding to the nose of the airplane) is rotated to show the true heading being flown.

To illustrate more fully how three bearings are set up and plotted with this protractor, the same three bearings used in Fig. 50 will be employed.

Three *relative* bearings are taken as follows: on station *A*, Cincinnati, 280°; on station *B*, Goshen, 350°; and on station *C*, Detroit (Wayne County), 70°. The magnetic heading is 280°. Knowing the approximate area of the airplane's position, the pilot obtains from the chart a variation of 3° west.

1. Calculate the true heading. This is 277° (280 − 3).

2. Set the 0 of scale *B* opposite 277 on scale *A* to represent the airplane's true heading.

3. One arm of the protractor is set on scale *B* to 280, representing the relative bearing of 280° on Cincinnati.

4. In like manner, the other two arms are set on scale *B* to represent the relative bearings on Goshen and Detroit.

5. When the protractor has been set, it is placed on the chart so that the meridians on the base plate are parallel to the meridians on the chart and also so that each arm of the protractor falls over the proper station. A dot made by inserting a sharp pencil through the hole in the center of the protractor denotes the fix.

Frequently, it is impossible to line up all three protractor arms over their respective stations while maintaining the base plate truly aligned with the meridians on the chart. Minor errors in the bearings, airplane movement while the bearings are being taken, or compass error may all contribute to this. Only experience in taking and plotting bearings will assist one to evaluate properly the effect of each of these factors.

Sometimes when a fix becomes doubtful owing to overly large accumulation of such errors, it is a help to plot the position by using successively different *pairs* of the three bearings combined with the heading. In this way, each plot will produce a fix at a slightly different location. The three locations arrived at thus form a triangle as happened in Fig. 50. This is usually termed a "triangle of error." Most probable position is at the center and thus is used as a fix.

Fix with Three Relative Bearings.—As was mentioned previously, the three-arm protractor allows a fix to be plotted with three relative bearings and no heading. When the heading is unknown because of compass failure, or it is suspected that compass error may be responsible for fixes of doubtful accuracy, this method should be tried. All that need be done is to set up the three relative bearings on scale *B* of the protractor as previously explained. Without considering the alignment of the base plate with the chart meridians, place the protractor on the chart so that the three arms fall over their respective stations.

Plotting without using a heading is recommended only in an emergency or to check for possible compass error when a fix plotted with a heading does not work out satisfactorily. *Without using the heading, it is possible to fall into a situation where the position is indeterminate.* This happens when the position of the airplane and all three stations are located approximately on the circumference of the same circle. Such a problem is known as a "revolver."

The Advantages of the Three-Arm Protractor.—Position plotting with the three-arm protractor has several advantages which should be apparent. In the first place, when combined with a proper plotting board, it is very much easier to use in the cockpit than other methods. Secondly, it makes the drawing of actual lines of position unnecessary and thus keeps the chart free of pencil marks. Very much more important, however, is the fact that with this device it is possible to plot positions with relative bearings. The protractor itself performs all the needed conversions to true or magnetic bearings. Once the method of setting up the bearings is understood, the whole process of plotting fixes is made more rapid and positive than other methods which require arithmetical conversion from relative to magnetic or true bearings and computation of reciprocals.

MERCATOR CHART PLOTTING

As explained previously, radio bearings follow the arc of a great circle across the earth's surface. Since any arc of a great circle is represented as a straight line on all aeronautical charts based upon the Lambert Conformal Conic projection, it is correct to plot lines of bearing on such charts as straight lines.

Outside the limits of the United States, however, a large percentage of charts used for navigation are constructed on the principle of the Mercator projection. This is particularly so for charts of oceanic areas.

On this type of chart, due to the projection method, a straight line between two points represents a so-called "rhumb line" rather than the arc of a great circle. The rhumb line by definition is one that intersects all meridians throughout its length at the *same angle*. Any arc of a great circle, on the other hand, must be represented on a Mercator chart as a curved line connecting the two points in question.

In actual practice, no attempt is made to plot a radio bearing on a Mercator chart as a curved line between the location of the transmitter and the direction finder. Instead, the bearing is plotted as a straight line on the chart *as if it had arrived at the direction finder via the rhumb-line track*. To do this, the angular difference at the direction finder between this rhumb-line track and the great-circle track is calculated; this value is then applied as a correction to the observed bearing so that it may be drawn on the chart as a straight (or rhumb) line.

In practice, it is not necessary to make this calculation

since tables have been computed to furnish the desired correction factor by inspection (refer to Table I). To use this table proceed as follows:

  1. Calculate by dead reckoning the probable latitude and longitude of the airplane when the bearing was taken.

  2. Using the known latitude and longitude of the ground station, calculate the difference in longitude between the ground station and the airplane as well as the mid-latitude between the two. Sufficient accuracy is obtained if these values are taken to the nearest whole degree.

  3. Enter the table at the top with the nearest whole degree difference in longitude.

  4. Move down this column until opposite the proper mid-latitude, and pick out the correction to be applied to the observed bearing.

  5. Read the rules printed below the table to determine whether the correction is added to or subtracted from the observed bearing.

  6. The corrected bearing may then be plotted on the Mercator chart as a straight line.

  Example: Assume that an aircraft is located approximately at latitude 39° 30′ north and longitude 70° 10′ west. A bearing of 294° true is taken on the La Guardia, N. Y., radio range station which is located at latitude 40° 43′ north and longitude 73° 55′ west. Find the correction from Table I so that the bearing may be plotted on a Mercator chart.

  1. The difference of longitude between the airplane's approximate position and the radio station is 3° 45′. Use 4° to enter table.

  2. The mid-latitude between the airplane's approximate position and the station is 40° 07′. Use 40° to enter table.

  3. By entering Table I with the above values, a correction of 1.3° is obtained.

  4. Since the airplane is in north latitude and east of the station, the rule printed below the table specifies that the

correction will be subtracted from the observed bearing of
294°.

5. Plot the bearing on the Mercator chart as 293° toward
the station since it is impractical to attempt more accurate
plotting with the average protractor.

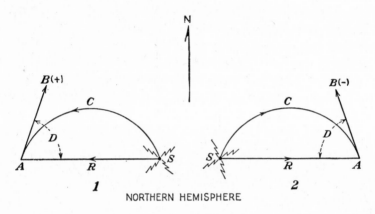

NORTHERN HEMISPHERE

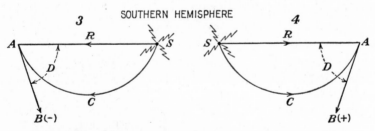

SOUTHERN HEMISPHERE

C *Great circle course followed by radio wave*
R *Desired rhumb line for plotting*
S *Location of station*
A *Location of direction-finder*
D *Correction angle taken from Table I*

FIG. 51.—Corrections to bearings for mercator chart plotting.

For those who may wish to verify the rules specifying the
sign of the correction printed below Table I, Fig. 51 has been
included.

TABLE I.—CORRECTION TO BE APPLIED TO RADIO

Mid. lat., deg.	Difference of longitude, deg.													
	1°	1.5°	2°	2.5°	3°	3.5°	4°	4.5°	5°	5.5°	6°	6.5°	7°	7.5°
4	. . . .	. . . .	. . . .	0.1	0.1	0.1	0.1	0.2	0.2	0.2	0.2	0.2	0.2	0.3
5	0.1	0.1	0.1	0.1	0.1	0.2	0.2	0.2	0.2	0.2	0.3	0.3	0.3	0.3
6	0.1	0.1	0.1	0.1	0.2	0.2	0.2	0.2	0.3	0.3	0.3	0.3	0.4	0.4
7	0.1	0.1	0.1	0.2	0.2	0.2	0.3	0.3	0.3	0.3	0.4	0.4	0.4	0.5
8	0.1	0.1	0.1	0.2	0.2	0.2	0.3	0.3	0.3	0.4	0.4	0.4	0.5	0.5
9	0.1	0.1	0.1	0.2	0.2	0.2	0.3	0.3	0.4	0.4	0.5	0.5	0.6	0.6
10	0.1	0.1	0.1	0.2	0.2	0.3	0.4	0.4	0.4	0.5	0.5	0.6	0.6	0.6
11	0.1	0.1	0.2	0.2	0.3	0.3	0.4	0.4	0.5	0.5	0.6	0.6	0.7	0.7
12	0.1	0.1	0.2	0.3	0.3	0.4	0.4	0.5	0.5	0.6	0.6	0.7	0.7	0.8
13	0.1	0.2	0.2	0.3	0.3	0.4	0.4	0.5	0.6	0.6	0.7	0.7	0.8	0.8
14	0.1	0.2	0.2	0.3	0.4	0.4	0.5	0.6	0.6	0.7	0.7	0.8	0.8	0.9
15	0.1	0.2	0.3	0.3	0.4	0.4	0.5	0.6	0.6	0.7	0.7	0.8	0.9	1.0
16	0.1	0.2	0.3	0.4	0.4	0.5	0.6	0.6	0.7	0.8	0.8	0.9	1.0	1.0
17	0.2	0.2	0.3	0.4	0.4	0.5	0.6	0.6	0.7	0.8	0.9	1.0	1.0	1.1
18	0.2	0.2	0.3	0.4	0.5	0.5	0.6	0.7	0.8	0.8	0.9	1.0	1.1	1.2
19	0.2	0.2	0.3	0.4	0.5	0.6	0.6	0.7	0.8	0.9	1.0	1.1	1.1	1.2
20	0.2	0.2	0.3	0.4	0.5	0.6	0.7	0.8	0.8	0.9	1.0	1.1	1.2	1.3
21	0.2	0.3	0.4	0.5	0.5	0.6	0.7	0.8	0.9	1.0	1.1	1.2	1.2	1.4
22	0.2	0.3	0.4	0.5	0.6	0.6	0.8	0.8	0.9	1.0	1.1	1.2	1.3	1.4
23	0.2	0.3	0.4	0.5	0.6	0.7	0.8	0.9	1.0	1.1	1.2	1.3	1.4	1.5
24	0.2	0.3	0.4	0.5	0.6	0.7	0.8	0.9	1.0	1.1	1.2	1.3	1.4	1.5
25	0.2	0.3	0.4	0.5	0.6	0.7	0.8	1.0	1.0	1.2	1.3	1.4	1.5	1.6
26	0.2	0.3	0.4	0.6	0.6	0.8	0.9	1.0	1.1	1.2	1.3	1.4	1.5	1.6
27	0.2	0.3	0.4	0.6	0.7	0.8	0.9	1.0	1.1	1.2	1.4	1.5	1.6	1.7
28	0.2	0.4	0.5	0.6	0.7	0.8	0.9	1.1	1.2	1.3	1.4	1.5	1.6	1.8
29	0.2	0.4	0.5	0.6	0.7	0.8	1.0	1.1	1.2	1.3	1.4	1.6	1.7	1.8
30	0.2	0.4	0.5	0.6	0.8	0.9	1.0	1.1	1.2	1.4	1.5	1.6	1.8	1.9
31	0.2	0.4	0.5	0.6	0.8	0.9	1.0	1.2	1.3	1.4	1.6	1.7	1.8	1.9
32	0.3	0.4	0.5	0.7	0.8	0.9	1.1	1.2	1.3	1.4	1.6	1.7	1.8	2.0
33	0.3	0.4	0.6	0.7	0.8	1.0	1.1	1.2	1.4	1.5	1.6	1.8	1.9	2.1
34	0.3	0.4	0.6	0.7	0.8	1.0	1.1	1.2	1.4	1.5	1.7	1.8	2.0	2.1
35	0.3	0.4	0.6	0.7	0.9	1.0	1.2	1.3	1.4	1.6	1.7	1.9	2.0	2.2
36	0.3	0.4	0.6	0.7	0.9	1.0	1.2	1.3	1.5	1.6	1.8	1.9	2.1	2.2
37	0.3	0.4	0.6	0.8	0.9	1.1	1.2	1.4	1.5	1.6	1.8	2.0	2.1	2.2
38	0.3	0.5	0.6	0.8	1.0	1.1	1.2	1.4	1.5	1.7	1.8	2.0	2.2	2.3
39	0.3	0.5	0.6	0.8	1.0	1.1	1.2	1.4	1.6	1.7	1.9	2.1	2.2	2.4
40	0.3	0.5	0.6	0.8	1.0	1.1	1.3	1.4	1.6	1.8	1.9	2.1	2.2	2.4
41	0.3	0.5	0.6	0.8	1.0	1.2	1.3	1.5	1.6	1.8	2.0	2.1	2.3	2.5
42	0.3	0.5	0.7	0.8	1.0	1.2	1.3	1.5	1.7	1.8	2.0	2.2	2.3	2.5
43	0.3	0.5	0.7	0.8	1.0	1.2	1.4	1.5	1.7	1.9	2.1	2.2	2.4	2.6
44	0.4	0.5	0.7	0.9	1.1	1.2	1.4	1.6	1.7	1.9	2.1	2.2	2.4	2.6
45	0.4	0.5	0.7	0.9	1.1	1.2	1.4	1.6	1.8	2.0	2.1	2.3	2.5	2.6
46	0.4	0.5	0.7	0.9	1.1	1.3	1.4	1.6	1.8	2.0	2.2	2.3	2.5	2.7
47	0.4	0.6	0.7	0.9	1.1	1.3	1.5	1.7	1.8	2.0	2.2	2.4	2.6	2.8
48	0.4	0.6	0.8	0.9	1.1	1.3	1.5	1.7	1.8	2.1	2.2	2.4	2.6	2.8
49	0.4	0.6	0.8	1.0	1.1	1.3	1.5	1.7	1.9	2.1	2.3	2.5	2.6	2.8
50	0.4	0.6	0.8	1.0	1.1	1.3	1.5	1.7	1.9	2.1	2.3	2.5	2.7	2.9
51	0.4	0.6	0.8	1.0	1.2	1.4	1.6	1.8	2.0	2.1	2.3	2.5	2.7	2.9
52	0.4	0.6	0.8	1.0	1.2	1.4	1.6	1.8	2.0	2.2	2.4	2.6	2.8	3.0
53	0.4	0.6	0.8	1.0	1.2	1.4	1.6	1.8	2.0	2.2	2.4	2.6	2.8	3.0
54	0.4	0.6	0.8	1.0	1.2	1.4	1.6	1.8	2.0	2.2	2.4	2.6	2.8	3.0
55	0.4	0.6	0.8	1.0	1.2	1.4	1.6	1.8	2.1	2.2	2.4	2.7	2.9	3.1
56	0.4	0.6	0.8	1.0	1.2	1.4	1.7	1.9	2.1	2.3	2.5	2.7	2.9	3.1
57	0.4	0.6	0.8	1.1	1.2	1.5	1.7	1.9	2.1	2.3	2.5	2.7	2.9	3.2
58	0.4	0.6	0.8	1.1	1.3	1.5	1.7	1.9	2.1	2.3	2.6	2.8	3.0	3.2
59	0.4	0.6	0.8	1.1	1.3	1.5	1.7	1.9	2.2	2.4	2.6	2.8	3.0	3.2
60	0.4	0.6	0.9	1.1	1.3	1.5	1.7	2.0	2.2	2.4	2.6	2.8	3.0	3.2
61	0.4	0.7	0.9	1.1	1.3	1.5	1.8	2.0	2.2	2.4	2.6	2.8	3.1	3.3
62	0.4	0.7	0.9	1.1	1.3	1.5	1.8	2.0	2.2	2.4	2.6	2.9	3.1	3.3

If the bearings are taken *at the airplane*, the sign of the correction to be applied to the bearing is as follows:

In *north latitude* when the airplane is $\frac{\text{eastward}}{\text{westward}}$ of the radio station, the correction is $\frac{\text{subtractive}}{\text{additive}}$.

Bearing to Convert to Mercator Bearing

| Difference of longitude, deg. | | | | | | | | | | | | | | Mid. lat., deg. |
8°	8.5°	9°	9.5°	10°	10.5°	11°	11.5°	12°	12.5°	13°	13.5°	14°	14.5°	
0.3	0.3	0.3	0.3	0.3	0.4	0.4	0.4	0.5	0.5	0.5	0.5	0.5	0.5	4
0.4	0.4	0.4	0.4	0.4	0.5	0.5	0.5	0.5	0.6	0.6	0.6	0.6	0.6	5
0.4	0.5	0.5	0.5	0.6	0.6	0.6	0.6	0.6	0.7	0.7	0.7	0.7	0.8	6
0.5	0.5	0.6	0.6	0.6	0.6	0.7	0.7	0.8	0.8	0.8	0.8	0.9	0.9	7
0.6	0.6	0.6	0.7	0.7	0.7	0.8	0.8	0.8	0.9	0.9	1.0	1.0	1.0	8
0.6	0.7	0.7	0.8	0.8	0.8	0.9	0.9	1.0	1.0	1.0	1.1	1.1	1.2	9
0.7	0.7	0.8	0.8	0.9	0.9	1.0	1.0	1.1	1.1	1.1	1.2	1.2	1.3	10
0.8	0.8	0.8	0.9	1.0	1.0	1.1	1.1	1.2	1.2	1.3	1.3	1.4	1.4	11
0.8	0.9	0.9	1.0	1.0	1.1	1.2	1.2	1.3	1.3	1.4	1.4	1.5	1.5	12
0.9	1.0	1.0	1.1	1.1	1.2	1.3	1.3	1.4	1.4	1.5	1.6	1.6	1.7	13
1.0	1.0	1.1	1.2	1.2	1.3	1.4	1.4	1.5	1.5	1.6	1.7	1.7	1.8	14
1.0	1.1	1.2	1.2	1.3	1.4	1.5	1.5	1.6	1.6	1.7	1.8	1.8	1.9	15
1.1	1.2	1.2	1.3	1.4	1.5	1.5	1.6	1.7	1.7	1.8	1.8	1.9	2.0	16
1.2	1.2	1.3	1.4	1.5	1.6	1.6	1.7	1.8	1.8	1.9	2.0	2.1	2.2	17
1.2	1.3	1.4	1.5	1.6	1.6	1.7	1.8	1.9	2.0	2.0	2.1	2.2	2.3	18
1.3	1.4	1.5	1.6	1.6	1.7	1.8	1.9	2.0	2.1	2.2	2.2	2.3	2.4	19
1.4	1.5	1.5	1.6	1.7	1.8	1.9	2.0	2.1	2.2	2.3	2.4	2.4	2.5	20
1.4	1.5	1.6	1.7	1.8	1.9	2.0	2.1	2.2	2.3	2.4	2.5	2.6	2.6	21
1.5	1.6	1.7	1.8	1.9	2.0	2.1	2.2	2.3	2.4	2.5	2.6	2.7	2.8	22
1.6	1.7	1.8	1.8	2.0	2.1	2.2	2.3	2.4	2.5	2.6	2.7	2.8	2.9	23
1.6	1.7	1.8	1.9	2.0	2.2	2.3	2.4	2.5	2.6	2.7	2.8	2.9	3.0	24
1.7	1.8	1.9	2.0	2.1	2.2	2.4	2.5	2.6	2.7	2.8	2.9	3.0	3.1	25
1.8	1.9	2.0	2.1	2.2	2.3	2.4	2.6	2.7	2.8	2.9	3.0	3.1	3.1	26
1.8	1.9	2.1	2.2	2.3	2.4	2.5	2.6	2.8	2.9	3.0	3.1	3.2	3.4	27
1.9	2.0	2.1	2.2	2.4	2.5	2.6	2.7	2.9	3.0	3.1	3.2	3.4	3.5	28
1.9	2.1	2.2	2.3	2.4	2.6	2.7	2.8	3.0	3.1	3.2	3.3	3.4	3.6	29
2.0	2.1	2.2	2.4	2.5	2.7	2.8	2.9	3.0	3.2	3.3	3.4	3.6	3.7	30
2.1	2.2	2.3	2.5	2.6	2.7	2.9	3.0	3.1	3.3	3.4	3.5	3.7	3.8	31
2.1	2.2	2.4	2.5	2.6	2.8	3.0	3.1	3.2	3.4	3.5	3.6	3.8	3.9	32
2.2	2.3	2.4	2.6	2.7	2.9	3.0	3.2	3.3	3.4	3.6	3.8	3.9	4.0	33
2.2	2.4	2.5	2.6	2.8	3.0	3.1	3.3	3.4	3.6	3.7	3.8	4.0	4.1	34
2.3	2.4	2.6	2.7	2.9	3.1	3.2	3.3	3.5	3.6	3.8	3.9	4.1	4.3	35
2.4	2.5	2.6	2.8	2.9	3.1	3.3	3.4	3.6	3.7	3.9	4.1	4.2	4.3	36
2.4	2.6	2.7	2.9	3.0	3.2	3.4	3.5	3.7	3.8	4.0	4.1	4.3	4.5	37
2.5	2.6	2.8	2.9	3.1	3.3	3.4	3.6	3.8	3.9	4.1	4.2	4.4	4.6	38
2.5	2.7	2.8	3.0	3.2	3.3	3.5	3.7	3.8	4.0	4.2	4.3	4.5	4.6	39
2.6	2.7	2.9	3.1	3.2	3.4	3.6	3.8	3.9	4.1	4.2	4.4	4.6	4.8	40
2.6	2.8	3.0	3.1	3.3	3.5	3.6	3.8	4.0	4.2	4.3	4.5	4.7	4.8	41
2.7	2.8	3.0	3.2	3.4	3.6	3.7	3.9	4.1	4.2	4.4	4.6	4.8	4.9	42
2.7	2.9	3.1	3.2	3.4	3.6	3.8	4.0	4.1	4.3	4.5	4.7	4.8	5.0	43
2.8	3.0	3.1	3.3	3.5	3.7	3.9	4.0	4.2	4.4	4.6	4.8	5.0	5.1	44
2.8	3.0	3.2	3.4	3.5	3.7	3.9	4.1	4.3	4.5	4.7	4.8	5.1	5.2	45
2.9	3.1	3.2	3.4	3.6	3.8	4.0	4.2	4.4	4.6	4.8	4.9	5.1	5.3	46
2.9	3.1	3.3	3.5	3.7	3.9	4.1	4.2	4.4	4.6	4.8	5.0	5.2	5.4	47
3.0	3.2	3.4	3.5	3.7	3.9	4.1	4.3	4.5	4.7	4.9	5.1	5.3	5.5	48
3.0	3.2	3.4	3.6	3.8	4.0	4.2	4.4	4.6	4.8	5.0	5.2	5.4	5.6	49
3.1	3.2	3.4	3.6	3.8	4.1	4.2	4.5	4.6	4.8	5.1	5.3	5.5	5.7	50
3.1	3.3	3.5	3.7	3.9	4.1	4.3	4.5	4.7	4.9	5.1	5.3	5.5	5.8	51
3.2	3.4	3.6	3.8	4.0	4.2	4.4	4.6	4.8	5.0	5.2	5.4	5.6	5.8	52
3.2	3.4	3.6	3.8	4.0	4.2	4.4	4.6	4.8	5.1	5.3	5.4	5.7	5.9	53
3.2	3.4	3.6	3.8	4.1	4.3	4.5	4.7	4.9	5.1	5.3	5.6	5.8	6.0	54
3.3	3.5	3.7	3.9	4.1	4.4	4.6	4.8	5.0	5.2	5.4	5.6	5.8	6.1	55
3.3	3.5	3.7	3.9	4.2	4.4	4.6	4.8	5.1	5.2	5.5	5.7	5.9	6.1	56
3.4	3.6	3.8	4.0	4.2	4.5	4.7	4.9	5.1	5.3	5.5	5.8	6.0	6.2	57
3.4	3.6	3.8	4.0	4.2	4.5	4.7	4.9	5.1	5.4	5.6	5.8	6.0	6.3	58
3.4	3.6	3.8	4.1	4.3	4.6	4.8	5.0	5.2	5.4	5.6	5.9	6.1	6.3	59
3.5	3.7	3.9	4.1	4.3	4.6	4.8	5.0	5.2	5.5	5.7	5.9	6.2	6.4	60
3.5	3.8	4.0	4.2	4.4	4.6	4.9	5.1	5.3	5.5	5.8	6.0	6.2	6.5	61
3.6	3.8	4.0	4.2	4.5	4.7	4.9	5.1	5.4	5.6	5.8	6.1	6.3	6.5	62

In *south latitude* when the airplane is $\frac{\text{eastward}}{\text{westward}}$ of the radio station, the correction is $\frac{\text{additive}}{\text{subtractive}}$.

If the bearings are taken by a radio direction finding station on the aircraft transmitter, the sign of the correction given above is reversed.

In the Northern Hemisphere, radio waves, or great circles, are always convex toward the north pole. The reverse is true in the Southern Hemisphere. Referring to Fig. 51, a series of exaggerated diagrams is shown to establish the correction sign. In diagram 1 in the Northern Hemisphere, the radio direction finder A is assumed to be to the westward of the transmitter. Since the observed bearing has traveled to the direction finder over the great circle track SCA, the direction of the bearing as observed at A is AB. The rhumb-line track from the radio station to the direction finder is the straight line SRA. In this instance, considering point A as the center of a compass rose, it will be apparent that the angular directional value of AS is greater than AB. Therefore, the angle D is the correction to be *added* to the observed great circle bearing to obtain the rhumb-line bearing for a Mercator chart. The same reasoning may be applied to diagrams 2, 3, and 4 to obtain the correction sign when the airplane and ground station are located in different relationship to each other or in the Southern Hemisphere.

CHAPTER IX

THE RUNNING FIX

A running fix is obtained by taking two or more bearings on either the same or different stations with an appreciable time interval elapsing between bearings. As this statement implies, running fixes may be divided roughly into two general types.

The first and most simple type of running fix is that obtained when two or more bearings are taken on two or more stations. This procedure differs very little from that followed for an instantaneous fix. In this instance, a proper allowance must be made for the movement of the airplane between the time of taking the first and last bearings. In practice, then, this would mean that whenever this time interval is much longer than 2 minutes (or the ground distance covered in this interval is more than 5 miles) the bearings should be plotted as a running rather than an instantaneous fix.

The second general classification of running fixes includes several different means of obtaining a fix by taking successive bearings on the same station. All these resolve into a simple solution of a triangle. Such a solution may be achieved by actual plotting, using precomputed tables, or very often, by the familiar navigational computers used for dead reckoning calculations.

Running Fix Using Two Stations.—An extremely simple method of establishing a position by a running fix is shown in Fig. 52. Two different bearings are taken on two different radio stations, A and B. The first bearing of 350° true (omitting all conversions for clarity) is taken on station A at 10:30. This places the airplane at some indeterminate position on the line of bearing 350° (line AA) toward station A.

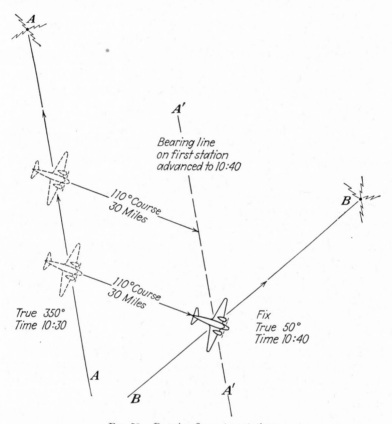

Fig. 52.—Running fix on two stations.

A second bearing of 50° true is obtained on station B at 10:40. Thus at 10:40 the airplane is placed at some indeterminate position on the line of bearing 50° (line BB) toward station B. During this interval between bearings, the airplane has been making good a course of 110° and a groundspeed of 180 miles per hour.

Obviously the intersection of the lines of bearing (AA and BB) does not represent a fix, since the airplane has moved during the 10 minutes intervening between the first and second bearings and at 10:40 is no longer on the original 350° bearing line toward station A.

We obtain a fix in this situation as follows:

1. Plot line AA representing a 350° bearing on station A at 10:30.

2. Plot line BB representing a 50° bearing on station B at 10:40.

3. Using the ground speed being made good, calculate the distance the airplane has moved *along the course line* in the time interval between bearings. In this example, it is 30 miles (180 miles per hour).

4. Lay out this distance ahead along the course line from the point where the course line is crossed by the first bearing line AA.

5. Draw a line $A'A'$ parallel to AA 30 miles advanced along the course line. This represents the 350° bearing on station A advanced to 10:40. Use a broken line to distinguish lines that have been advanced from the original bearing line.

6. Since line AA has now been advanced in a direction and distance representative of the airplane's movement between 10:30 and 10:40, its intersection with BB will represent the fix at 10:40.

Suggestions on Moving Lines of Bearing.—It will be apparent that, if desired, the fix could have been established in the preceding example as of 10:30 by moving the second bearing *back* along the course, rather than advancing the first bearing. Likewise, both bearings may be advanced or retarded in similar fashion if a fix is wanted at some other time which does not coincide with the time of either bearing.

Such a procedure would be used if it were necessary to establish the fix at some predetermined time as required by a position-reporting schedule. For instance, oceanic flights customarily report their positions at a definite time each hour rather than at definite check points as in domestic operation. If in the example illustrated by Fig. 52 such a schedule called for a position as of 10:45, it would be evident that both lines of bearing should be advanced to this time. Thus the first bearing would be advanced 15 minutes and the second 5 minutes.

Two very important considerations should always be kept in mind when moving lines of bearing. (1) A line that has been advanced or retarded is only as accurate as the ground speed and course used in moving it. Use care that lines are not moved for a longer time than necessary—a 10-minute maximum is suggested. (2) Always remember that the distance a line is moved is *always measured along the course.*

Another suggestion when using navigational procedures of this type is to label each line of bearing with the time it was taken, and if advanced, the time to which it was advanced. During long flights, care in such details becomes essential.

ONE STATION FIX

Running fixes using two bearings taken at different times on the same radio station lend themselves advantageously to aircraft navigation. Once the general principles governing the several variations of this procedure are understood, obtaining a fix in this manner becomes very simple to execute in actual practice.

Principles Involved.—Reference to the figures that follow will disclose that all these procedures for establishing a fix with only one station resolve to nothing more than the solution of a triangle. Two points of any such triangle are determined by the position of the airplane at the moment of taking each bearing; the third point is the radio station. In like manner, two sides of the triangle represent the airplane's distance from the radio station at the moment each bearing is taken. The third side represents the distance flown by the airplane between the two bearings.

As a general rule, such a navigational triangle is easily solved when the following information is known:

1. Distance flown between the two bearings. This naturally is obtained as the product of ground speed and time between bearings.

2. The *course* made good during the problem. This is obtained by applying the amount of wind drift to the true heading.

3. The angular difference between the first and the second bearings.

The disadvantage of this type of position fix should be apparent immediately. Its accuracy is dependent upon two factors in addition to the radio bearings. These are an assumption of ground speed and course being made good. Obviously, under conditions when a fix of this type might be most desired, an accurate ground speed and course might not be known.

Notwithstanding the fact that this type of position fix is much less accurate than other types previously described, it possesses sufficient merit to warrant inclusion in any pilot's fund of knowledge. (1) Only one radio station need be used. This might be a real advantage when it is difficult to take bearings on more than one station. (2) Certain of the procedures to be explained are so simple that a pilot may obtain the information he desires without even plotting the bearings on the map. Such simple methods are extremely convenient and fully practical when accuracy is not the most important consideration.

Running Fix on One Station.—In Fig. 53 a typical running fix obtained with two bearings on the same station is diagramed. A pilot in an airplane assumed to be making good a true course of 130° and a ground speed of 180 miles

per hour obtains a true bearing of 170° on station S at 10:10.
A second bearing of 275° true is obtained on the same station at 10:29.

Required: the airplane's position at 10:29.

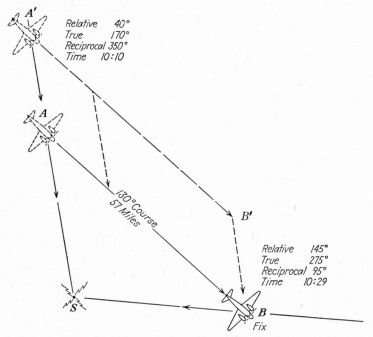

FIG. 53.—Running fix one station.

1. Convert both true bearings into their reciprocals, and plot from the station as lines of indeterminate length SAA' (350°) and SB (95°).

2. Calculate the distance flown in 19 minutes (10:29–10:10) at 180 miles per hour. This is 57 miles.

3. Using the graphic scale on the chart, set a pair of dividers (or mark a piece of paper) to represent a distance of 57 miles. This line (represented by the length AB or $A'B'$ in the figure) is the one known side of the triangle to be completed and is also the side opposite to the angle ASB.

4. The length of the two remaining sides *SA* and *SB* may be found by *maintaining this 57-mile line parallel to the course line* while simultaneously sliding it across the chart until its length exactly joins the two bearing lines, thereby establishing points *A* and *B*. This completes the triangle *ASB*.

5. Point *B* is the fix at 10:29.

Obviously, once the points *A* and *B* have been established by plotting, the distance from the station at either the moment of the first or second bearing may be scaled from the chart as lengths *SA* and *SB*, respectively.

Distance from Station Problem.—In Fig. 54 is illustrated a special type of running fix on one station designed primarily to inform a pilot how far to one side he has passed a station as at point *A* or his direction and distance from a station as at *B*.

Although this type of problem like the previous one may be solved by graphical plotting on the chart, its very simplicity makes this unnecessary. The problem in practice is always executed so that the two positions of the airplane (*A* and *B*) when bearings are taken make a right triangle with the station (*S*). Then, since a right triangle is easily solved either by tables or with navigational computers so familiar to pilots, plotting is not resorted to.

Referring to Fig. 54, the following might be a typical problem. The pilot desires to know at what distance he will pass a radio station which is to the left of his course. The airplane's course is 90° true and the heading 80°. The ground speed is 180 miles per hour. The detailed steps of the problem are as follows:

1. Set the loop-null position to a relative bearing that will provide a 90° angle to the airplane's *course*. This will be 280° on the azimuth scale.

2. Note the time the null is received. This is the first bearing and places the airplane on the line of bearing *SA* (180°) or exactly broadside to the station. Assume that the time is 12:02.

3. Maintain the same heading and course for 2, 3, or 5 minutes. Any other even interval of time may be used. In practice, the time interval selected will be that one necessary to achieve a definite change of bearing on the station. In this example, let us assume 5 minutes.

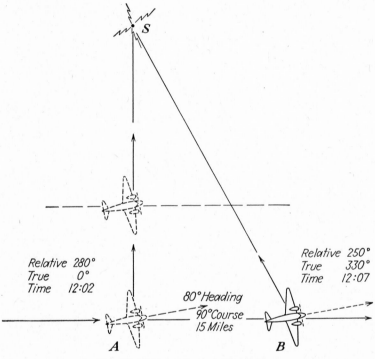

Fig. 54.—Distance from station problem.

4. At the time interval selected, rotate the loop to obtain a new bearing on the station S and note the number of degrees by which this differs from the first bearing. By assuming that the first bearing is 280° relative and the second 250° relative, this angle in our problem becomes 30°.

5. Calculate the distance flown during the time interval between the first and second bearings (positions A and B).

TABLE II.—DISTANCE FROM STATION TABLE

Italic figures indicate mileage from station at start of problem; roman figures indicate mileage from station at end of problem.

Bearing Change, deg.	Ground Speeds														
	120 miles per hour			140 miles per hour			160 miles per hour			180 miles per hour			200 miles per hour		
	2 min.	3 min.	5 min.	2 min.	3 min.	5 min.	2 min.	3 min.	5 min.	2 min.	3 min.	5 min.	2 min.	3 min.	5 min.
5	*45.5* 46	*68.5* 69	*114.5* 115	*53.5* 54	*79.5* 80	*132.5* 133	*60.5* 61	*91.5* 92	*152.5* 153	*68.5* 69	*102.5* 103	*171.5* 172	*76.5* 77	*114.5* 115	*194.5* 195
10	*22.5* 23	*34* 34.5	*56.5* 57.5	*26.5* 27	*40* 40.5	*66* 67	*29.5* 30	*45.5* 46	*74* 76.5	*34* 34.5	*51* 52	*84* 86.5	*38* 38.5	*56.5* 57.5	*96.5* 98
15	*15* 15.5	*22* 23	*37.5* 38.5	*17.5* 18	*26* 27	*43.5* 45	*20.5* 21	*30* 31	*49* 51	*22* 23	*34* 35	*56* 58	*25* 26	*37.5* 38.5	*63.5* 66.5
20	*11* 12	*16.5* 17.5	*27.5* 29	*13* 14	*19.5* 20.5	*32* 34	*15* 16	*21.5* 23	*36.5* 39	*16.5* 17.5	*25* 26.5	*41.5* 44	*18.5* 19.5	*27.5* 29	*46.5* 49.5
25	*8.5* 9.5	*12.5* 14	*22* 24	*10* 11	*15* 16.5	*25* 27.5	*12.5* 11.5	*17* 19	*29* 32	*12.5* 14	*19* 21	*32* 35.5	*14.5* 16	*22* 24	*36.5* 40
30	*7* 8	*10.5* 12	*17.5* 20	*8.5* 10.5	*12* 14	*20* 23	*9.5* 11	*14* 16	*23* 26.5	*10.5* 12	*15.5* 18	*26* 30	*11.5* 13.5	*17.5* 20	*29.5* 34
35	*5.5* 7	*8.5* 10.5	*14.5* 17.5	*6.5* 8	*10* 12	*16.5* 20	*7.5* 9	*11.5* 14	*19* 23	*8.5* 10.5	*12.5* 15.6	*21.5* 26	*9.5* 11.5	*14.5* 17.5	*24* 29.5
40	*4.5* 6	*7* 9.5	*12* 15.5	*5.5* 7.5	*8.5* 11	*14* 18	*6.5* 8.5	*9.5* 12.5	*15.5* 20.5	*7* 9.5	*10.5* 14	*18* 24	*8* 10.5	*12* 15.5	*20.5* 26.5
45	*4* 5.5	*6* 8.5	*10* 14	*4.5* 6.5	*7* 10	*11.5* 16.5	*5.5* 7.5	*8* 11.5	*13.5* 19	*6* 8.5	*9* 12.5	*15* 21.5	*6.5* 9.5	*10* 14	*17* 24
50	*3.5* 5	*5* 8	*8.5* 13	*4* 6	*6* 9	*9.5* 15	*4.5* 7	*6.5* 10.5	*11* 17.5	*5* 8	*7.5* 11.5	*12.5* 19.5	*5.5* 9	*8.4* 13	*14.2* 22
60	*2.5* 4.5	*3.5* 7	*6* 11.5	*2.5* 5.5	*4* 8	*6.5* 13.5	*3* 6	*4.5* 9	*7.5* 15.5	*3.5* 7	*5* 10.5	*8.5* 17.5	*4* 8	*5.8* 11.5	*9.8* 19.5

NOTE: Distances in the table are calculated to the nearest ½ mile.

Example: A pilot wishes to determine his distance from an off-course radio station at the moment of passing it. The loop is set so that the null position is at 90° to the airplane's *course*. The time is noted when the null is received. Three minutes are flown on the same course, and the bearing on the station is found to change 30°. The ground speed is 140 miles per hour.

Solution: Enter the table at the top, using 140 miles per hour ground speed and the 3-minute subdivision of this column. Move down the column until opposite 30° change of bearing found on the left of the table. Read the upper figure, 12 miles, as the distance from the station at the first bearing, and the lower figure, 14 miles, as the distance from the station at the second bearing.

This is easily done on any calculator by using the ground speed and the time flown. This is 15 miles (side AB of the triangle).

6. The angular change in bearing between positions A and B is identical to angle ASB of the triangle. By using this and the length of the side AB just calculated, both the sides SA and SB can be solved. These are, respectively, the distance of the airplane from the station at the time of taking the first and second bearings. The distance at the time of taking the first bearing is 26 miles, and the distance from the station at the time of taking the second bearing is 30 miles. Any navigational computer may be used to do the above arithmetic.

If it is desired, the line of bearing from the point B to the station may be plotted. Then laying out the calculated distance on this line from the station will provide a geographic position fix at B.

Table II shows how this same problem may be solved without a calculator. The disadvantage of the table, of course, is that interpolation is necessary when the ground speed comes in between those for which the table was calculated. The use of the table is self-explanatory.

45-degree Problem.—A second type of special running fix may, for want of a better name, be called the 45° problem. From an inspection of Fig. 55, it will be seen that this is only another variation of the previous problem designed to provide an easy method of obtaining distance from a radio station, or if desired, a geographic fix. This method of working the problem does, however, provide two distinct advantages over the method just described.

(1) The amount of calculation needed to solve the problem is again reduced. (2) The information really wanted, *i.e.*, the airplane's distance from the station at the moment of passing it, is obtained at the most desirable time (the moment the airplane passes the station).

To achieve this result, the problem is actually set up prior to reaching the station. The following might be a typical example. A pilot desires to know at what distance he is

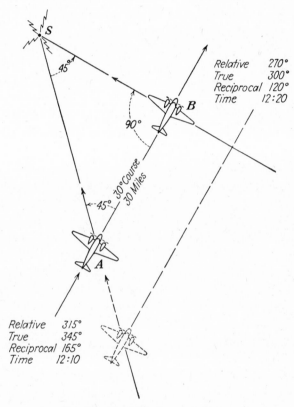

Fig. 55.—Forty-five degree problem.

passing a radio station which is to the left of his course. The airplane's course and likewise the heading is 30° true, and the ground speed is 180 miles per hour. The detailed steps are as follows:

1. Set the loop-null position to a relative bearing that will provide a 45° angle to the airplane's *course*. This will be

315° on the azimuth scale. This operation must be done at a point well in advance of a point opposite the station.

2. Note the time when a null on the station is received. Assume that this is 12:10.

3. Continue to fly this heading and course. While doing so, reset the loop position so that a second null will be obtained when the station is at 90° to the course. In Fig. 55, the azimuth pointer in this position will read 270° on the scale.

4. Note the time of obtaining this second null—in this problem, 12:20.

5. Calculate the distance flown in the time interval between the first and second bearings. This will be the product of 180 miles per hour for 10 minutes, or 30 miles.

6. By using this procedure, the distance of the airplane from the station at the time of the second bearing (SB) is the same as the distance flown between the first and second bearing. Therefore, the airplane is 30 miles from the station at the moment of passing it.

In the same manner as the other problems, the geographical fix at B may be obtained by plotting if desired.

The reason that the computation is so simple in this problem is because ASB is an isosceles triangle in which the angle BAS equals the angle BSA. This, of course, makes the side AB equal the side SB.

Doubling Angle Off the Course.—Figure 56 illustrates another special type of running fix. This again consists of setting up a definite sequence of bearings on one station in order to obtain the desired information without recourse to plotting the bearings on a chart and with a minimum of calculation. Although this type of problem is very closely related to the last two explained above, it in turn possesses some distinctive advantages.

The purpose of this procedure is to provide a pilot with a simple means of calculating his distance from a station located ahead of him and at one side of the course *prior to passing it.* In addition, he may calculate ahead to determine at what time and what distance he will pass the station.

Figure 56 represents a typical problem. A pilot wishes to know what his distance from an off-course radio station will be at some time prior to passing it. He also wishes to know at what time and distance he will pass it. The airplane's

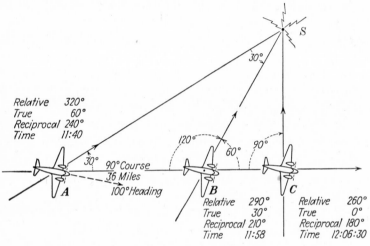

Relative   320°
True   60°
Reciprocal 240°
Time   11:40

90° Course
36 Miles
100° Heading

Relative   290°
True   30°
Reciprocal 210°
Time   11:58

Relative   260°
True   0°
Reciprocal 180°
Time   12:06:30

Fig. 56.—Doubling angle off the course.

course is 90° true while flying a heading of 100°. The ground speed is 120 miles per hour. The detailed steps in solving this follow:

1. Well ahead of the station as at position *A*, a bearing is taken on the station which proves to be 30° to the left of the *course.* This, as seen in the diagram, will be a relative bearing of 320° on the azimuth scale. Assume that the time is 11:40.

2. Maintain the same course and ground speed, and set the loop-null position to a relative bearing on the azimuth scale which will *exactly double the first angle off the course.* The relative bearing in this example would be 290°.

3. Note the time—in this problem 11:58—when the null signal indicates that the desired second bearing has been achieved. The airplane will be at position *B*.

4. Calculate the distance flown in the time interval between bearings. At 120 miles per hour for 18 minutes, the distance will equal 36 miles. This is side *AB* of the triangle *ABS*.

5. The distance from the station at the time of the second bearing (point *B*) equals the distance flown between the two bearings—36 miles.

It will be seen that the proper execution of this procedure has again made *ABS* an isosceles triangle. This may be proved by further reference to the figure.

The three angles of any triangle always total 180°. At the start of the problem, the angle *BAS* was 30°. Since the angle *CBS* is 60° when the airplane is at point *B*, the angle *ABS* must equal 120°. We now have two angles of the triangle *ABS* totaling 150°. Therefore, the angle *ASB* must equal 30° and the sides *AB* and *BS* are equal.

This problem is very familiar to marine navigators who usually refer to it as "doubling the angle off the bow." In air-navigation practice, however, care must be used in this as well as all other running fixes of this nature to employ bearing angles *off the course* of the airplane rather than off the bow or nose of the airplane. This is due to the considerable difference which may exist between an airplane's heading and course because of wind.

Whereas an angle of 30° off the course was obtained on the first bearing for the example cited, other angles may be used in similar fashion. Usually any angle between 10 and 40° off the course can be used initially as long as twice this angle is set up for point *B*. Obviously, when a 45° angle is used initially, this problem becomes the 45° problem explained above.

Having ascertained his distance from the station at the point *B*, a pilot can immediately calculate what his distance from the station will be when passing it and the time this will occur.

Referring again to the figure, the side BS of the triangle BSC is already known from the previous solution. The angle CBS is also known. The angle SCB at the moment of passing the station must be 90°. Since these two angles total 150°, the remaining angle BSC is found to be 30°. Once more, sufficient information is available to solve for the remaining two sides of the triangle CS and BC. These are, respectively, the distance of the airplane from the station at the time of passing it and the distance that must be flown from point B to point C.

By translating the preceding facts into different form, it will be apparent that as the airplane moves from point B to C the bearing on the station must change by 30°. As we have proved before, this change of bearing is equal to the angle CSB in the triangle. Again, the two unknown sides of the triangle may be found by use of a navigational computer in a manner similar to that suggested for a previous example. Or, if desired, a table can be devised to accomplish the same result.

Actually, there is a slight difference in this latter solution of a right triangle from that previously used. Before, the known information was the angle of bearing change and the distance flown between bearings. In this problem, the known information is the distance from the station at the start of the problem (side BS of the triangle) and the two angles CBS and CSB. However, if sufficient knowledge of a computer is possessed to enable the solution of one problem, no difficulty should be experienced in solving the other.

Thus, by solving for these sides BC and CS, in the problem illustrated by Fig. 56, the distance from the station at the moment of passing it is found to be 31 miles and the distance to be flown from B to C is 18 miles. Then, since it will take 9 minutes to fly 18 miles at 120 miles per hour, the time of passing the station will be 12:07.

CHAPTER X

THE RADIO COMPASS

The radio compass is a refinement of the aural-null direction finder designed to eliminate the 180° ambiguity of bearing indication. In other words, a direction-finder furnishes a pilot with only a line of bearing through an airplane's position and the radio station without establishing on which side of the airplane the station is located (refer to Fig. 29, Chap. VI). The double pointer used with the direction-finder azimuth dial is a constant reminder of this limitation. A radio compass, however, provides a pilot with a bearing on a station which is free from ambiguity.

The advantage of the radio compass over a direction finder in actual practice should be apparent. As long as radio reception can be maintained on a radio station, the location of which is marked on a pilot's maps, he is continuously oriented. Theoretically, this eliminates the need for orientation procedures; actually, a pilot must know these in order to be prepared for the numerous emergency situations that can arise in actual practice.

A second major advantage of the radio compass is that a visual-null indicator is provided in addition to aural reception. This makes null determination with a radio compass easier and more accurate than with aural-null direction finders.

Operating Principles.—A radio compass in simplest form is nothing more than a direction finder to which certain features have been added to eliminate ambiguity of bearing indication. Whereas the direction finder is based entirely upon the directional reception qualities of the loop antenna, a radio compass uses such a loop in conjunction with a non-directional T antenna.

Sperry automatic-radio-compass loop housing. (*Courtesy of American Airlines, Inc.*)

Referring to Fig. 57, the component parts of a radio compass are illustrated. These are a shielded loop antenna, an unshielded nondirectional T antenna, an azimuth control unit, and a left-right indicator. A view of a hypothetical

radio-compass receiver-control panel has also been included
for reference in subsequent explanation. In Fig. 57 is also

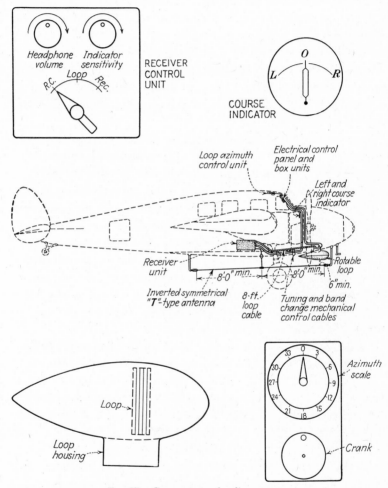

Fig. 57.—Components of radio compass.

shown a typical aircraft installation. If structural factors
require, the loop and T antenna may be mounted on the top
of the fuselage.

The additional features incorporated in a radio compass as compared with an aural-null direction finder are seen to be the T antenna and the left-right indicator.

With all electrical theory being omitted, the purpose of the nondirectional T antenna used in conjunction with a directional loop is to provide unidirectional bearing indication. Radio energy picked up separately on each antenna is fed into a specially designed receiver circuit which is capable of "detecting" from which side of the loop the incoming radio waves are arriving.

The left-right indicator provides the pilot with a visual means to *interpret* this selective response of the receiver unit. He then knows which of the two possible bearing indications is the correct one toward the station. In addition to its "sensing" action, the indicator provides a visual means of locating the null that is more accurate than aural reception.

Operation of the Radio Compass.—The operation of a simple radio compass is basically similar to the aural-null direction finder. In fact, any radio compass can be used as an aural-null direction finder by either disregarding the left-right indicator or by disconnecting it from the circuit by means of a selector switch provided for that purpose.

A generalized description of the manner in which a simple radio compass is used follows (refer to Figs. 57 and 58).

1. Place the receiver unit in operation as a *regular range* (or broadcast) *receiver* by means of a selector switch provided on the receiver control unit (selector switch on *REC* in Fig. 57). Tune in and identify the station.

In this position, the T antenna alone is being used.

2. Place the selector switch on the *LOOP* position, and rotate the loop by azimuth crank until an aural null is obtained on the station. With the selector switch in the *LOOP* position, the *loop only* is being used and the equipment is being employed as a simple aural-null direction finder. The left-right indicator is disconnected.

Referring to Fig. 58, it will be assumed for illustration that the aural-null bearing places the station directly in line with the airplane's longitudinal axis. The relative bearing on the azimuth scale will then read either 0 or 180°. In other words, the station position is either directly ahead of or directly behind the airplane. The problem is to establish which is the true location of the station.

3. Change the selector switch to radio compass operation (R.C.). Now both antennas and the left-right indicator will be incorporated in the circuit. If the aural-null bearing has been established accurately, the needle on the indicator will be centered. If necessary, however, center it by a final slight adjustment of the loop position so that an exact null is established.

4. Rotate the loop about 10° either to the right or left while watching the motion of the needle on the left-right indicator. Refer to Fig. 58, which is a diagram of the military-system needle action. If the station is *ahead* of the airplane, *the needle will move to the left as the loop is rotated to the right,* and vice versa. The needle always points toward the station. If the station is to the *rear* of the airplane, *the needle will move to the right as the loop is rotated to the right,* and vice versa. It will be seen that the needle still points toward the station (reverse end of needle).

In Fig. 59 is diagramed the action of the needle on the left-right indicator usually found in commercial installations. Although the operation of the radio compass is similar in all respects to that explained above, the needle action on the indicator is diametrically opposite to the military system. This is often termed the "turn-indicator system" since the needle action is in harmony with that of the turn indicator.

Whereas it is only necessary to reverse the wires connected to the left-right indicator to change its action, it is particularly important for a pilot to make certain which system is

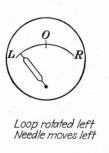

Loop rotated left
Needle moves left

Loop rotated right
Needle moves right

Station behind airplane

 Station

Station ahead of airplane

Loop rotated left
Needle moves right

Loop rotated right
Needle moves left

Fig. 58.—Indicator reading, military system.

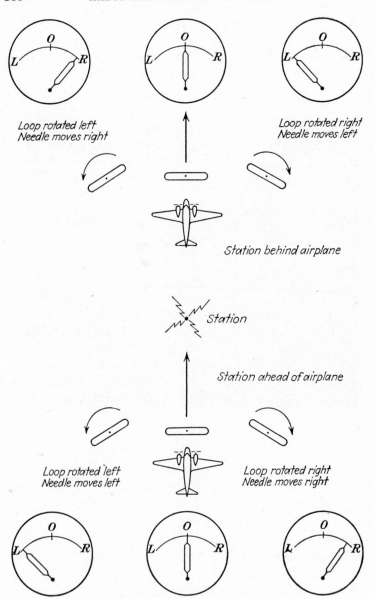

Loop rotated left
Needle moves right

Loop rotated right
Needle moves left

Station behind airplane

Station

Station ahead of airplane

Loop rotated left
Needle moves left

Loop rotated right
Needle moves right

FIG. 59.—Indicator reading, commercial system.

being used in any radio-compass-equipped airplane before attempting any radio compass problem.

Additional Details of Operation.—The summarized operating instructions given above can be regarded as applying to all radio compasses. The operating details of any particular

Radio-range instruction—Link Trainer. (*Courtesy of American Airlines, Inc.*)

make of radio compass must be studied, however, in order to operate it properly. As such instructions are beyond the scope of this text, it is suggested that the instruction manual explaining the operation of the equipment a pilot expects to use be closely examined.

Most radio compasses, regardless of manufacture, include one additional control that was not mentioned in the above summary. This is to govern the sensitivity of the left-right indicator. In Fig. 57, such a control is shown on the receiver control unit panel. With this a pilot may adjust the sensitivity and thus the deflection of the indicator needle to compensate for signal intensity or to eliminate an oversensitive needle action in turbulent air. The normal procedure when taking bearings is to adjust the needle sensitivity so that full deflection is produced in either direction when the loop is rotated about 30°. This adjustment must be altered from time to time as distance to or from the station is changed.

Although it has not been specifically mentioned, it should be apparent from the foregoing discussion that most radio-compass receiving equipment may be used not only as a radio compass but at the choice of the pilot as either a standard range receiver or an aural-null direction finder. Many radio compasses also cover the commercial-broadcast frequency bands.

An additional radio-compass feature not mentioned prior to this is simultaneous aural reception of a station signal while maintaining a visual-null bearing on the station. When the equipment is placed in radio-compass operation, a circuit is so designed that normal station reception is maintained in the pilot's headphones by the nondirective T antenna. Only the visual indicator is used to establish the null.

Although numerous other salient features are present in various types of equipment, it is felt that a better presentation of these will be found in the proper instruction manuals.

AUTOMATIC RADIO COMPASSES

Several advanced types of radio compass have been developed in recent years which will provide a pilot with continuous and automatic radio-compass bearings on any station within the frequency and sensitivity ranges of the receiver. To provide a brief and nontechnical presentation of this type of equipment, a summarized description of the Sperry Automatic Radio Compass follows.

General Features.—This equipment consists of a combined control and indicating unit, a sense antenna, a specially designed receiver, and a *pair* of shielded loops mounted within a streamlined housing.

Fig. 60.—Latest type indicator and control unit for the single automatic direction finder. When once tuned to a station, the indicator on this device points continuously to the station tuned. As the Sperry direction finder is automatic in operation, the pilot is only required to refer to it to determine his position.

The control and indicator unit is designed for mounting in a horizontal plane on the throttle column of the average transport airplane (refer to Fig. 60). In this position it may be operated and observed conveniently by both pilots.

The sense antenna, a balanced T, is usually of the same type as that used with any radio compass. Customary transport mounting is on the underside of the fuselage.

The streamlined housing shielding the loops is also mounted on the underside of the fuselage. The use of two loops fixed at 90° to each other is a novel departure from previous radio compasses and makes possible several desirable operating features.

The receiver unit is specially designed for use with this equipment. Although the details of design and construction are too intricate to permit explanation in this text, some of the salient features of equipment operation which it makes possible are as follows:

1. Fully automatic and continuous radio-compass bearings on any radio station to which the receiver is tuned.

2. Automatic and continuous direction finding under precipitation static conditions.

3. Manual aural-null direction finding.

4. Anti-static loop reception on the maximum position.

5. Standard beacon and broadcast band reception as a regular receiver.

Automatic Operating Features.—Operating as an automatic radio compass, the control unit is designed to provide the pilot with fully automatic and continuous visual bearings on any station to which the receiver is tuned. Bearings are indicated by a pointer moving through a 360° azimuth scale.

The pointer is connected by a flexible shaft to the loop assembly, which is fitted with a motor controlled by the receiver output. The action of the motor-control circuits brings the loop to a null position on any station to which the receiver is tuned. This null is continuously and automatically maintained, without 180° ambiguity and irrespective of changes in the airplane's heading.

The equipment may be operated as an automatic visual direction finder under static conditions. By means of a selector switch, the unshielded sense antenna is disconnected and a second shielded loop substituted. Bearings, however, are subject to the 180° ambiguity common to all direction finders. The second loop, used to replace the sense antenna, is mounted in the streamlined housing on the same shaft with the null loop but displaced from it by an angle of 90° (refer to Fig. 61). As a result of this arrangement, continuous headphone signal is provided by the second loop, which is

Fig. 61.—Dual loop assembly.

maintained at the position of maximum pickup relative to the station.

When in automatic operation or operating on broadcast stations, a visual meter is provided for precise tuning.

Indicator Unit Features.—The indicator unit combines in a single centralized location all controls, indicators, and navigation scales that are used in the operation of the equipment.

The azimuth scale is of the 360° type (unless the 180° left and right type is requested) graduated evenly throughout. Quadrantal errors of the loop are compensated by a specially cut cam built into the base of the indicator unit between the loop drive cable and the azimuth pointer.

Navigational Scales.—In addition to the usual azimuth scale fixed in relation to the airplane's longitudinal axis, the indicator face also incorporates a movable scale and a variation index scale to assist in the conversion of relative bearings to true or magnetic bearings. By setting up these scales properly in advance, it is possible to read either magnetic or true bearings directly off the indicator.

Fig. 62.—Use of scales to read magnetic bearings.

Fig. 63.—Use of scales to read true bearings.

Referring to Figs. 62 and 63, two examples illustrate the use of the navigational scales.

1. To obtain the magnetic bearing of a station, the movable inner scale is rotated so that the magnetic heading of the airplane is opposite 0° on the variation scale. The pointer then indicates the relative bearing on the outer fixed scale

and the magnetic bearing on the inner scale. In the example illustrated by Fig. 62, the magnetic heading is 20°, the relative bearing 60°, and the magnetic bearing 80°.

2. To obtain the true bearing of a station, the movable inner scale is rotated so that the magnetic heading of the airplane is *opposite the compass variation* on the variation index scale. The pointer then indicates the relative bearing on the outer fixed scale and the true bearing on the inner scale. In the example illustrated by Fig. 63, the magnetic heading is 30° and the compass variation is 10° west. The relative bearing is 70°, and the true bearing is 90°.

Advantages of the Automatic Radio Compass.—The automatic radio compass may be used with equal facility for homing or for taking bearings to ascertain the geographic position of the airplane. It does for the navigator what the automatic pilot does for the human pilot, *i.e.*, it reduces the number of duties he has to perform and permits him to supervise a series of operations rather than being forced to perform them himself.

Its greatest advantage, of course, lies in the fact that once tuned to a station it continues to indicate the direction of that station, irrespective of the airplane's heading or the progress of the airplane over the ground. The loop of the ordinary radio compass or direction finder, on the other hand, must be manually adjusted to the null position whenever it is desired to take a bearing. Likewise, the continuous, automatic, nonambiguous bearing is a tremendous aid in solving orientation problems. The pilot sees at a glance the relative and magnetic bearings of the range station throughout the problem, and quadrant identification becomes a simple matter. Strictly speaking, orientation problems are eliminated.

The automatic radio compass also checks a cone of silence unmistakably, the pointer swinging around 180° and pointing in the opposite direction in the time it takes for an airplane to cross the cone of silence.

INDEX

A

Adcock radio range, 11
  physical appearance of, 12
Antennas, 9
  nondirectional, 10
  T type, 157, 161
  theory of loop, 10
Anti-static, position of loop for, 80
Aural null loop, 79
  basic operating principles of, 80
Azimuth, loop, 80, 86, 90, 94

B

Beam, selecting nearer, 105
Beam bracketing, 27
  under drift conditions, 30
  summary of, 32
  with timed turns, 29
  unknown beam, 62
Beam techniques, 24–41
Beams, bending of, 19
  convergence on, 25
  multiple courses of, 19
  shifting of, 19
  swinging of, 19
Bearings, distance from station problem, 145
  doubling angle off the course, 150
  45° problem, 148
  moving lines of, 141
  plotting from assumed position, 124
  plotting at the radio station, 124
  plotting techniques, 123
  preparation prior to taking, 116
Bisectors, average, 44, 62
  determination of, 45

C

CAA, 23
  publications of, 23
Charts, special D/F, 128
Coast-line error, bearings, 93
Cone of silence, 17, 108
  false, 20
Course to station, ascertaining, 102

D

Direction finders, aircraft, 7
  ground, 7, 92
  technique with, 121
Direction finding, 6, 7, 79–93
  basic concepts of, 94
  distance from station by, 145
  inaccuracies of, 91

F

Fading, 19
Fan type marker, 21

G

Great circle, 133
Ground wave, 91

H

Heaviside layer, 91
Homing, 106

I

Indicator, left-right, 157
  commercial system of, 158
  military system of, 158
  sensitivity of, 161